WOLSEY  LODGES

WELCOME

For over 30 years Wolsey Lodges have been welcoming guests into their homes.
Arriving as strangers, many guests leave as friends. Our reputation for hospitality
in some of the finest homes to be found has meant our circle of friends has grown and grown.

We welcome you to turn the page and discover Wolsey Lodges for yourself.

relax • explore • indulge • experience • enjoy

Many reasons to stay and no reason to leave

Romantic break away; family holiday; birthday celebrations; anniversary surprise; a base for touring the area - there are many reasons why our guests choose Wolsey Lodges.

Whatever your reason for staying in a Wolsey Lodge you will find a warm welcome awaits you and sets the theme for your whole stay.

However you decide to spend your time, your Wolsey Lodge hosts will do all they can to make a world of difference to the overall enjoyment of the place you stay. And, if you are celebrating a special occasion, make sure you inform your host when you book so that you can arrange with them those extra touches to make your stay truly special.

Arrive and know you may not wish to leave.

Left: Esplanade House, Essex (Wolsey Lodge)

GREAT EXPECTATIONS

We understand what makes a good bed and breakfast become an unbelievable bed and breakfast and it all comes down to experience. We expect great things of all of our Lodges because they expect it of themselves. To each and every one of our hosts, the service they offer is a way of life and not just a way of working.

Our hosts open their homes to you and unreservedly commit themselves to making it your home - ensuring that you relax and enjoy your time with them from the moment you arrive.

Quietly comfortable, lavishly luxurious, invariably elegant and filled to the brim with the homely touches that our hosts know, from experience, make all the difference in the world to their guests - sumptuous towels in the bathrooms, beds made up with the finest linen, books, games and music to entertain.

Serenity in summer, warmth in winter, delicious home-cooked food, dinner party atmospheres if you dine in the evening, blissful bedrooms, pristine bathrooms, a comfortable sitting room and peaceful gardens to arouse your senses.

Our standards are exacting as we have a lot to live up to.

Our own team of inspectors personally visit each and every Lodge to ensure they continue to offer everything our guests expect.

Many of our Lodges also invite VisitBritain and/or AA assessors to visit them and endorse our own inspector's exacting standards. These Lodges have been awarded four or five stars and some have silver and gold awards as well.

Serenity in summer, warmth in winter

From top: Hawkhill House, Oxfordshire (Wolsey Lodge); Skirling House, Lanarkshire (Wolsey Lodge); Hrempis Farm, Leicestershire (Wolsey Lodge); Pentillie Castle, Cornwall (Wolsey Lodge)

iii

FIRST IMPRESSIONS

Every one of our Wolsey Lodges is a unique private home and the very nature of this uniqueness, some may call it quirkiness, is what our guests have come to expect, and indeed return to, so often.

We want you to be happy with us from the moment you first make contact and so, to make life a little easier, we have compiled the following pages of notes that will help you to understand what to expect from your stay at a Wolsey Lodge.

Each Wolsey Lodge has its own page in this book which aims to give you a flavour of what you can look forward to when you stay there. On each page you will find out about your hosts and what facilities they have and whether the Lodge is suitable for children, if dogs are welcome, or if evening meals will be available to you.

Quietly comfortable, lavishly luxurious & always elegant

Wolsey Lodges will typically have a minimum of two bedrooms available for their guests, each usually made up with duvets, but please ask if you would prefer sheets and blankets.

Many hosts will provide tea, coffee, fruit juices and other lovely touches such as fruit and homemade biscuits in your room. Don't expect to find a fridge, however, hosts will usually provide fresh milk when you need it.

All rooms will have en suite or private bathrooms (if the bathroom is private you'll normally find fluffy bathrobes waiting for you) but some may have either a shower or bath, so if you have a preference, please discuss it when you book. Towels, fragrant bathroom bubblies, soap and shower gels are usually all supplied.

If you are travelling with friends or relatives and are happy to share a bathroom with them, then your hosts may be able to accommodate you. It is always worth asking your hosts if there are rooms available during your stay so everyone in your party can be accommodated. Alternatively your hosts may be able to help you arrange accommodation for large parties at several closely located Lodges - so just ask.

In line with 'no smoking' legislation in England, Scotland and Wales, all Wolsey Lodge accommodation is 'smoke free' with the majority of houses showing the symbol 🚭 which indicates that it is a No Smoking House. However, a small number of Wolsey Lodges show the 🚭 symbol which means that whilst all rooms used by guests are totally smoke free, smoking may occur in other, private parts of the house.

Sleeping, showering or soaking in the bathtub - relaxation is assured

Left: Hovington House, Wiltshire (Wolsey Lodge)

The sumptuous surroundings to be found at Wolsey Lodges is equal only to the quality of the breakfasts that will follow your good night's sleep. Always fresh and often locally sourced or organic ingredients are offered, whether you opt for a light start to the day with fruit and cereals or plump for a hearty breakfast to see you through your day's activities.

Menus will vary considerably so please feel free to discuss your breakfast requirements with your hosts when you book especially if you have special dietary needs.

Joining us for dinner?

A long held tradition for Wolsey Lodge hosts is to offer their guests dinner at some point during their stay. Whilst for many Wolsey Lodges this tradition holds strong, the changing needs of guests mean that some will offer just a light supper, whilst others do not offer evening meals at all, but instead have a veritable array of nearby restaurants, bistros and bars to recommend to their guests.

Some Wolsey Lodges are licensed to sell alcoholic drinks (look for the 🍸 symbol in their entry) so lingering late over a final glass of fine port or aged brandy is not unusual. Prices for wine are generally as you would expect them to be in a pub and if the Lodge is not licensed, please check with your hosts about bringing your own drink. This is indicated by the BYO symbol in their entry.

If the Lodge you are staying at offers dinner or supper then you can expect a culinary treat in the company of other guests and sometimes your hosts as well. The number of courses and the nature of the evening meal will vary from Lodge to Lodge and this is reflected in the price.

Each Lodge is unique in what it offers and so we strongly recommend that you discuss your dining requirements with your host when you book to avoid later misunderstandings and disappointment. If you have agreed to 'dine in', then discuss with your hosts the exact nights you will be expecting dinner and any special dietary requirements that any member of your party has.

Your hosts will be able to offer you advice on the best places to enjoy a sumptious lunch.
Top: Old Whyly, East Sussex (Wolsey Lodge)

Visiting with your family - & the dog could come too.

Wolsey Lodges are located across the country making them an ideal base for touring an area. Some Wolsey Lodges welcome children although many will state a minimum age for their guests - this is shown on their entry page although it will always be at your hosts' discretion depending on the requirements of their other guests. It is essential you inform your hosts if there are children in your party.

If your hosts offer evening meals it is very possible that young children will not be able to dine with other guests, but your hosts may be able to provide a suitable meal at an earlier time for them or will suggest alternative venues. Wolsey Lodges that are suitable for children may offer cots and help with your baby (such as warming bottles and baby food in the kitchen) but it is essential that you discuss your requirements at the time of booking. Check too about price reductions for children, as these often apply!

You will find three symbols in the Lodges' entries that denote their policy on dogs and/or pets at their house. The symbol denotes that the house has no animals in it and do not take guests' dogs either. The symbol denotes that the Lodge has their own pets in the house but do not take guests' dogs. Finally if you want to take your own dog(s) with you then please look for the symbol. IMPORTANT NOTE - Even where this symbol appears, guests **must** discuss their requirements at the time of booking, as each Lodge will have their own policy about where in the house guests' pets can be taken - some Lodges do not allow dogs in the house and instead have kennels outside.

Top: Lost Gardens of Heligan, Cornwall.

Across to France

The magic of Wolsey Lodges can be found at an exclusive collection of Lodges in France.

These Lodges combine all the style, sophistication and hospitality that Wolsey Lodges has come to be known by, with easy continental charm; all located in some of the most idyllic and unspoilt areas of France.

Your hosts are all English-speaking and very knowledgeable about their areas to help you understand its history, culture, character and, of course, its cuisine.

Prices quoted on these members' pages will be in Euros and they will only accept payment in Sterling by prior arrangement. Please check the Sterling prices at the time of booking as exchange rates will vary.

Discover the magic of Wolsey Lodges across France

Reservations

Staying at a Wolsey Lodge is totally different to staying at an hotel and much of what makes a stay truly enjoyable comes from discussing your proposed visit with your hosts.

The easiest way to make your booking is by telephone which gives you the chance to check all of the details properly and ensure that you have chosen the right Lodge for your individual needs. Alternatively you can make a booking enquiry through the website (www.wolseylodges.com) by completing your details, required dates and your specific requirements. The individual Lodge will then contact you to progress your booking.

Booking is essential at all Wolsey Lodges as most will not accept guests without a pre-arranged booking.

Deposits

Your hosts will often ask for a non-refundable deposit to secure your booking, with the balance of payment due on departure.

Left: Chateau de la Barre, France (Wolsey Lodge)

On arrival

Normal arrival time is between 4pm and 6pm. It is essential that you let your host know the time you plan to arrive particularly if your arrival is likely to be later than 6pm. It's also worth noting that your hosts may well be out during the day and will not expect to greet you before 4pm at the earliest unless you have made definite alternative arrangements with them. You are visiting your hosts' home so when you arrive please ring the bell if your host hasn't already seen you, rather than walking straight in.

Your planned arrival time is especially important if you have arranged to 'eat-in' on your first evening as meals are served at a set time and a late arrival may mean that you miss your meal completely. Delays on journeys are a tiring annoyance but a call to your hosts to let them know of a delayed arrival is much appreciated and, whether you were planning to dine with them or not, it means they may be able to make alternative supper arrangements for you.

During your stay

If you are staying for a number of days, your hosts will still expect you to be out for most of the day as many of them will have work or shopping to do and will not have staff to attend to you in their absence. However, some are happy for you to spend your days around the Lodge to use the pool, tennis courts or perhaps to go walking, but please check this with your hosts carefully.

Departure

White Horse at Uffington, Oxfordshire.

You will normally be expected to vacate your room by 11am at the latest on your day of departure.

Cancellations

If you have to cancel your booking, please remember that a contract exists between you and the Wolsey Lodge that you have made your booking with. The Lodge will always try to re-let your cancelled accommodation, but your deposit will not normally be refunded due to the administration costs of making the initial booking and re-booking.

Wolsey Lodges recommend that all Lodges have a cancellation policy if they cannot re-let the accommodation you have booked. In these circumstances you will be liable for 30% of the total charge if you cancel within 28 days of the visit; 60% if you cancel within 13 days and 80% if you cancel within 48 hours.

Some Lodges may have their own cancellation policies that differ from this and this will be made clear to you when you make your reservation.

We do not operate a cancellation insurance scheme and strongly recommend that you take out your own appropriate cover.

Prices &
our latest
information

Prices

All prices shown on the Lodge information pages are per person, per night based on shared occupancy of a double or twin bedded room and include a generous 'Wolsey Lodge' breakfast. An extra charge is usually made for a double room used as a single, highlighted as 'Single supplement' or 'Single occupancy'. Reduced charges may apply for extended stays, so please check with the Lodge when booking. All prices are inclusive of VAT where applicable.

IMPORTANT - The prices shown in this brochure were correct at the time of going to print. We recommend that you confirm the prices when making your reservation. Where there is a price variance, Wolsey Lodges Ltd cannot be held responsible for any problem that may arise.

Visit our website

At www.wolseylodges.com you will find not only our complete brochure but a secure on-line shop where you can purchase gift vouchers as well as additional copies of this brochure. You will also find full details of any new additions to our Collection there.

Easy to navigate maps will help you to select your Lodge and allow you to plan your journey whether you are visiting just one Lodge or several, in the UK or France. An automatic booking enquiry form enables you to complete your details and your preferred dates of travel, and your selected Lodge will then contact you to progress your booking.

New Lodges

This year we have 9 new Lodges for you to discover and enjoy. All their details can be found in the index section at the back of the brochure where they are highlighted.

Alternatively you can of course view their details by visiting www.wolseylodges.com and clicking on 'Discover New Lodges'.

Helping with a problem

All Lodges take their standards of quality very seriously and so, should a problem arise during your stay, or if you have any comments regarding quality at the Lodge you stay in, you must first inform your host so that they can attempt to put the problem right.

Choose your Wolsey Lodge

We have designed this brochure to be as simple as possible to use - whether you wish to search by region, by Lodge name and number, or by UK county or country.

The book is arranged by country and county so if you want to stay in a particular area, simply turn to that section of the book.

House Name	County	Entry No.
Long Crendon Manor	Buckinghamshire	1

Finding your perfect Lodge is simple

Sue Soar
Long Crendon Manor
Frogmore Lane
Long Crendon
Aylesbury
Buckinghamshire
HP18 9DZ
Tel: 01844 201647 or 07867 521399
longcrendonmanor.co

There is also a full index at the back of the brochure and Lodge entries are entered numerically starting with Lodge Entry Number 1.

The Lodge Entry Numbers will change for each edition of this brochure but one number will always stay the same - this is the four digit booking reference number on each Lodge's page which can be found just below the address and contact numbers.
You can use this number when making a booking in the future but we do recommend you get a new edition of this brochure when it has expired to ensure you are referring to the most up to date information available.

On our website www.wolseylodges.com you will find a series of easy-to-use, detailed maps to show exactly where each Lodge is located.

Special offers

and so much more

There is something quite wonderfully decadent about taking a weekend break at short notice. Stepping out of your everyday world, re-charging your batteries and seeing and experiencing something a little out of the ordinary. Take a short, or long, break to any Wolsey Lodge and you will not only discover beautiful houses but also kind, attentive hosts who warmly welcome you into their homes.

Our e-Newsletter will continue to keep you informed throughout the year. You've particulary appreciated the highlights we have given to Lodges that may be offering something a little different such as special menus as local, seasonal produce becomes available, open garden days, Christmas and New Year invitations and late-availability breaks. We've also given readers new ideas for unusual places to visit and updates about new Wolsey Lodges to try.

To register for our e-Newsletter simply email info@wolseylodges.com

From top: Three Cliffs Bay, Gower Peninsula; Prawles Court, East Sussex (Wolsey Lodge); The Old Hall, Cambridgeshire (Wolsey Lodge).

Homes & owners that make the difference

Could your home be a Wolsey Lodge?

Wolsey Lodges was started by a group of like-minded owners in 1981. Since then we have built a reputation for the quality of our houses and, most importantly, the level of hospitality we offer our guests.

Individuality, quality, consistency, quiet elegance, comfort, attention to detail, a warm, friendly welcome - these are all the things we value and which we know make the ultimate difference to a guest's experience. Our Lodge owners come from all walks of life - individuals, couples, families - all with varying outlooks, hobbies and lifestyles. Some of our hosts have jobs away from the home, some work from home and others are retired, but they still all share a real dedication to ensuring their guests have a memorable time.

This dedication to our guests, the exceptional accommodation we offer combined with outstanding cuisine, have all contributed to building our excellent reputation.

If you already run a B&B or think that your home and your hospitality might be what our guests are looking for, we would be delighted to send you a copy of our prospectus.

Ideally you will need to have a minimum of two guest bedrooms (4 bed spaces), each with their own bathroom, preferably en suite. Whilst some Wolsey Lodges still offer the option of dinner or supper every night, many offer it only occasionally, while others opt not to offer evening meals at all, which means you have total flexibility about what you offer.

Please visit our website www.wolseylodges.com for full details or contact our administration office on 01473 822058 for a prospectus and application form. We look forward to hearing from you.

Top: Esplanade House, Essex (Wolsey Lodge)

WELCOME TO ENGLAND

Fabulous historic cities and towns, great country houses and gardens, bustling seaside resorts, picturesque villages, and miles and miles of beautiful countryside and coastline await your discovery throughout England.

Shopping, relaxing, exploring history, the best cuisine in the world - England has it all. Whichever area of England you choose to visit there will be far more to take in than time will ever allow. Rest assured though that your hosts' intimate knowledge of their area means that you will get first-hand, on-the-spot advice of the very best that there is to experience.

From top: King's College Chapel, Cambridgeshire; Birling Gap, East Sussex; Roman Baths, Bath

Sue Soar
Long Crendon Manor
Frogmore Lane
Long Crendon
Aylesbury
Buckinghamshire
HP18 9DZ
Tel: 01844 201647 or 07867 521399
sue.soar@longcrendonmanor.co.uk
www.longcrendonmanor.co.uk   4986

The Property

Visitors to Long Crendon Manor will find themselves stepping back in time to undoubtedly one of the oldest Wolsey Lodges to be found. Dating back to 1187 when it began life as the dwelling for the abbots of Notley, the east and west wings were added in later centuries before a total refurbishment began in 1920.

Sue Soar and friendly St Bernard Coco will welcome you with tea and homemade biscuits. The delightful guest rooms are spacious and cosy and each has an en suite bathroom. As well as tea, coffee and a carafe of sherry, a fridge is filled with treats (some complimentary and some charged). Supremely comfortable beds are adorned with fine linen and goose down duvets. One bedroom has an adjoining dressing room which could be used as a small twin for children – ideal for a family.

Outside the gardens include a maze, croquet lawn and swimming pool; a vegetable and fruit garden, meadow and Sue's collection of rare breed pigs. Guests can use the oak-panelled drawing room to relax, read, watch television or just enjoy the log fire on a cold winter's night. Breakfast is served in the beamed dining room off the medieval hall and in the summer can be served on the terrace beneath the vine.

The Hosts

Sue had a successful career as a hotelier and now dedicates herself to Long Crendon Manor and breeds traditional English rare-breed pigs. Tim runs his own interim executive business, and they have three children.

The Location

Long Crendon Manor is unique and has been used in many TV productions including Midsomer Murders. Close by is Waddesdon Manor, Oxford Botanic Gardens, Bicester Village, Claydon House, Blenheim Palace, Stowe Gardens, Oxfordshire Golf Club, the Ashmolean Museum, Bletchley Park and the University of Oxford.

Finding Us

From M40 Junction 8a, follow A418 towards Aylesbury. On outskirts of Thame at services roundabout take B4011 to Long Crendon. First left in the village at The Square and continue down Frogmore Lane. Long Crendon Manor stone archway is 50 yards on left.

Rooms (per person per night incl. breakfast)

3 Double Rooms (en suite)	£50
Single Occupancy	£80-£100

Meals

Dinner	£30

Opening Times

Occasionally closed Christmas

Payment Options

Facilities & Services

Tim and Henrietta Breitmeyer
Westoe Farm,
Bartlow, Cambridgeshire CB21 4PR
Tel: 01223 892731 or 07776 258666
Fax: 01223 892731
enquire@bartlow.u-net.com
www.westoefarm.co.uk   3988

Finding Us

Take the A1307 eastbound from A11 dual carriageway, towards Haverhill and Colchester. After 4 miles pass through the village of Linton and ½ mile after BP station turn right at the Bartlow crossroads. 1 mile to Bartlow, through the village and after 1 mile and third farm track on the right is the drive leading up to Westoe Farm

The Property

Tranquil views and afternoon tea with homemade cakes, biscuits and scones will greet you on arrival at Westoe Farm, a warm and very comfortable flint and brick farmhouse, surrounded by open land which is farmed by the family.

You will feel relaxed right away in this recently renovated family home where a separate wing on the ground floor, once the original cattle barn, provides beautifully furnished guest accommodation. Guests can also relax in the drawing room with the papers surrounded by the family's varied collection of African wildlife artefacts and paintings.

Albertine and Dreaming Spires climbing roses scramble over the walls, creating a fragrant veil over the house and adjoining barn. Beyond the tennis court and swimming pool, the open garden blends seamlessly into surrounding farmland and woods, perfect for an evening stroll.

Breakfast is cooked fresh to order and includes (amongst many other choices) eggs, bacon and sausages, all home reared, with the eggs cooked any way you prefer. Westoe Farm is well placed for eating out in the evenings with a selection of pubs close by and the hosts will happily make suggestions and reservations for you.

The Hosts

Tim and Henrietta are young, energetic and enthusiastic and entertain guests with the same verve and panache as they approach their many other interests. Tim spent 18 years in The Grenadier Guards serving in Northern Ireland and Germany before coming home to run the family farming business in 1996. Henrietta is a keen horsewoman and excellent cook, and runs a ski holiday business in France in the winter.

The Location

Westoe Farm is ideally situated for many attraction including Duxford Imperial Warm Museum, Cambridge and Newmarket Racing and Sales. It is also only 25 minutes from Stansted and would make a peaceful and enchanting stopover for longer haul travellers.

Rooms (per person per night incl. breakfast)

2 Double/Twin Rooms (en suite)	£55
Single occupancy	£75

Meals

Breakfast only

Opening Times

Closed Christmas & New Year

Payment Options

Facilities & Services

Mrs Alison Morbey
The Old Hall
Stuntney
Ely
Cambridgeshire CB7 5TR
Tel: 01353 663275
stay@theoldhallely.co.uk
www.theoldhallely.co.uk   3966

The Property

With uninterrupted views across to Ely Cathedral and steeped in history, The Old Hall is a restored Jacobean manor house that was once home to Oliver Cromwell's mother and which today offers a luxury B&B retreat for visitors to the Fens. The house and surrounding estate have been in the Morbey family since 1860 and your hosts Alison and Anthony started their renovations in 1999 on the footprint of the original manor house. Today the house's Jacobean heritage is artfully blended with modern luxury furnishings and décor.

The warm and comfortable guest bedrooms, one having a super four poster king size bed, are furnished with antiques and handmade furniture, fine linen and a tea tray laid with delicious homemade treats. Large en suite bathrooms have splendidly decadent baths as well as separate power showers and Molton Brown toiletries – a real delight. Each room overlooks the gardens to the front or back of the house and guests exploring the grounds will discover a network of walks around the formal garden and ornamental lakes. Afternoon Tea is served daily between 4.00 p.m. and 6.00 p.m. with scrumptious carrot cake a specialty.

The Hosts

Alison and Anthony have poured themselves into the renovations of The Old Hall and the work continues in the gardens where Alison is often found busily planning and planting. Anthony is a farmer, a keen shot and fisherman and enjoys bridge.

The Location

Ely is just one mile away, offering an excellent variety of restaurants and pubs for evening meals. The Cathedral, Cambridge Colleges, Wicken Fen Nature Reserve, Oliver Cromwell's House, Anglesey Abbey, Wimpole Hall and Welney Wetland Reserve are all close by. Newmarket and the National Stud for racing enthusiasts, Duxford Museum and fantastic walking countryside complete the picture for a visit to The Old Hall near Ely.

Finding Us

A142 One mile south of Ely, go past first sign into Stuntney village, the house is on the left hand side on a hill. Entrance is approximately 300 metres further on, with oak lattice gates set back from road. From Newmarket approach via A142, past southern entrance to Stuntney village and house is 300 metres on right. Please do not use Sat-Nav.

Rooms (per person per night incl. breakfast)

3 Double Rooms	(en suite)	**from £55**
1 Twin Room	(en suite)	**from £55**

Meals

Breakfast only

Opening Times

Closed Christmas & New Year

Payment Options

Facilities & Services

The Property

This elegant and comfortable 1830s Cornish country house stands in the rolling countryside of the Roseland peninsula.

Alison greets her guests and after showing them to their rooms, serves tea in the guest's drawing room.

The three guest bedrooms, all with their own generous bathrooms, are comfortable, inviting and prettily decorated, with superb views over the beautiful two acre garden.

This is Alison's first love and she delights in showing guests around. She has restored and enlarged it meticulously over the last twenty years. It contains many rare and interesting plants, a sunken, herbaceous walled garden, a croquet lawn and a recently laid-out potager.

The Hosts

Anthony has spent much of his professional life in East Africa and the Far East and has had his own law firm in Truro. A keen sailor and golfer he has a yacht in which a day's sailing may be arranged.

Alison has practised horticulture and garden design all her professional life. She holds a NDH and is an authority on Cornish plants and gardens. She will also happily recommend interesting places and restaurants to visit.

The Location

Tregoose is centrally situated for the whole county - from the Tate at St Ives and Land's End to houses and gardens on the Devon border - all are within an hour's drive. The great gardens of Caerhays, Heligan, Trewithen and the Eden Project are all within five miles and beaches, sailing waters and the coastal footpath are easily reached.

Anthony & Alison O'Connor
Tregoose,
Grampound, Truro, Cornwall TR2 4DB
Tel: 01726 882460
Fax: 01872 222427
tregoose@tregoose.co.uk
www.tregoose.co.uk   2995

Finding Us

Leave A30 by turning left for Grampound Road. Continue 5 miles through Grampound Road. Turn right at junction with A390 towards Truro. The lane leading to drive is after 200 yards, on right, just where double white lines end in centre of road; lane entrance is between four black and white reflector posts.

Rooms (per person per night incl. breakfast)

2 Double Rooms	£49-£63
(1 en suite/1 private)	
1 Twin Room (en suite)	£55-£63
Single Supplement	£20

Meals

Dinner	£32

Opening Times

Closed Christmas, New Year & Easter

Payment Options

Facilities & Services

Mike & Jan Russell
Penarwyn House
St Blazey,
Par,
Cornwall, PL24 2DS
Tel: 01726 814224
info@penarwyn.co.uk
www.penarwyn.co.uk   2968

Finding Us
From the A390 at St Blazey turn into Doubletrees school, drive down past the school, Penarwyn is directly in front of you.

Rooms (per person per night incl. breakfast)

3 Double/Twin Rooms (en suite)	£55-£80
Single Supplement for Double or Twin rooms	£30
1 Single Room (en suite)	£75

Meals
Breakfast only

Opening Times
Closed Christmas & New Year

Payment Options

Facilities & Services

The Property
Not content with being a gloriously restored Victorian house offering every modern comfort and luxury, Penarwyn is also the home of the most welcoming and delightful hosts one could wish to meet. Jan and Mike have created a wonderfully peaceful haven that is beautifully furnished and finished with careful attention to detail, which is reflected in the unsurpassed standard of service they offer their guests. Their aim is to make your stay so enjoyable and unforgettable that you will want to return again and again – and they certainly succeed in that.

From the first glimpse of the house from the driveway, the view of the gardens displaying a wide variety of native and sub tropical trees and shrubs, it is clear this is something special. The bedrooms and bathrooms are superbly furnished, offering televisions, DVD/CD players, tea and coffee making facilities, hairdryers, and luxurious baths and showers with fine linen, towels and robes. The drawing room has comfortable furniture, a Boudoir Grand piano and French doors opening onto the glazed veranda and guests are welcome to use the billiards room with its selection of books, games and puzzles. Breakfast at Penarwyn is award winning, freshly cooked and definitely not to be missed.

The Hosts
Mike and Jan entered the hotel industry in the early 1990's and have brought those years of experience to Penarwyn. Their skills in interior design and carpentry are evident throughout the house. They 'go the extra mile', from arranging pick ups for guests arriving by train and helping to plan days out to recommending local restaurants for dinner – nothing is too much trouble.

The Location
Perfect for the Eden Project, The Lost Gardens of Heligan, Lanhydrock House, and Carlyon Bay golf course. Visit Lostwithiel, Fowey, Charlestown, St Mawes and the Roseland Peninsula, Padstow and Lands End.

Mr & Mrs Ted Coryton
Pentillie Castle
St Mellion, Saltash
Cornwall PL12 6QD
Tel: 01579 350044 or 01579 212002
contact@pentillie.co.uk
www.pentillie.co.uk   **2962**

Finding Us

Take A38 into Cornwall. At first
roundabout, turn right onto A388, signed
to Callington and Launceston. Follow
road for 3.1 miles, to Paynters Cross. Turn
right signed Paynters Cross, Cargreen and
Landulph. Pentillie Castle gates are within
100 yards of main road.

The Property

The splendour and comfort of Pentillie Castle is absolutely
second to none. From the moment you arrive and drive
through the parkland with its abundance of oaks and views
across Dartmoor, to discovering the perfectly sumptuous
bedrooms, gardens and dining that await you, it is quite
possible you could wish to lose yourself here and never
leave.

The castle started life as a grand formal house in 1698 and
was gradually enlarged and used for different purposes
throughout the following centuries before it was inherited
and restored by hosts Ted and Sarah Coryton. Almost 55
acres of park, woodland and garden surround the castle
including a heated outdoor pool and an American garden
abundant with rhododendrons, camellias, magnolias and
azaleas. Inside, large though it is, there is a welcoming,
homely feel overlaid with an unmistakable historic grandeur.

Each guest room is luxurious, comfortable and spacious
with en suite bathrooms to match, thoughtfully filled
with scented toiletries. Breakfast and dinner are served in
the atmospheric setting of the dining room which in the
evening twinkles with candle light. Pentillie Castle is unlike
any other Wolsey Lodge and a real treasure to visit.

The Hosts

Ted and Sarah's love of Pentillie is clear in the work they
have done to make it their home and guests are made to
feel so welcome to share it with them and nothing is too
much trouble – just ask. Ted is a former helicopter pilot and
still works as an aviation and oil exploration consultant and
Sarah is a clinical massage therapist.

The Location

Exploring and enjoying the grounds here will take time, but
step away from the castle and close by are river trips on the
Tamar, Bodmin Moor and Dartmoor, The Eden Project,
National Trust properties and of course, the splendour of
Cornish gardens aplenty.

Rooms   (per person per night incl. breakfast)

4 Double/Twin Rooms (en suite)	£60-£100
1 Four Poster Double Room (en suite)	£100

Meals

Dinner (By prior arrangement)	from £30

Opening Times

Open all year

Payment Options

Facilities & Services

Mr & Mrs Peter Stanley
Mazey Cottage
Tangies
Gunwalloe
Helston
Cornwall TR12 7PU
Tel: 01326 565868
stanley.m2@sky.com
www.mazeycottage.co.uk   2960

Finding Us

A3083 Helston-Lizard. After 1 mile turn right opposite RNAS Culdrose entrance. Do not go under the bridge. Narrow steepening lane for just under 1 mile. House is on the right at the bottom of the steep hill.

The Property

Set amidst 3½ acres overlooking the oak woodland of Carminowe Valley, this tranquil eighteenth century farmhouse is home to Peter and Marion Stanley whose previous Cornish home was well known to Wolsey Lodge guests.

In the beamed sitting room a stylish log burner in the large inglenook blazes on cooler days when guests can sink into deep comfortable sofas adorned by colourful cushions. Antiques, books and flowers mingle with watercolours and finely chosen contemporary art which reflect Marion's interests - she can advise on local galleries, auctions and gardens. The effortless chic continues upstairs in a restful guest bedroom dressed with fine linen, which overlooks the walled front garden. The adjacent private bathroom has a free standing bath, thick towels and local organic toiletries.

Rambling roses cascade down steps into the valley with its babbling brook. On through the woodland walk, around the large pond, crossing bridges, through the orchard and kitchen garden to the summer house - Mazey Cottage is a gardener's delight. Guests are welcome to enjoy the garden at any time, seats are dotted throughout from where endless wildlife can be observed.

Rooms (per person per night incl. breakfast)

1 Double Room (private)		**£45-£55**
Single Supplement		**£15**

Meals

Supper	**£25**

Opening Times

Closed Christmas & New Year

Payment Options

Facilities & Services

The Hosts

Peter & Marion are relaxed and friendly hosts. Peter is a lively raconteur and keen sportsman involved in long distance cycling, kayaking and walking. Marion's passion is her garden, she also inspects for the National Garden Scheme and is a contributory writer for garden publications.

The Location

Surrounded by the National Trust woodlands, the sea, Loe Bar and Loe Pool (Cornwall's largest lake) are a ten minute walk. Nearby are Godolphin House, Trebah and Glendurgan Gardens, St Michaels Mount, Minack Theatre, Tate St Ives and Falmouth Maritime Museum. Water sports can be arranged for day sailing, canoeing, fishing or surfing.

Annabel & Jonathon Croggon
Creed House
Creed
Grampound
Truro
Cornwall
TR2 4SL
Tel: 01872 530372
jrcroggon@btinternet.com
www.creedhouse.co.uk   2958

The Property

Creed House is everything this beautiful part of the country offers. Set in seven acres of gardens, this spacious Georgian house was once home to the local rector before it became the family home of your hosts Annabel and Jonathon Croggon. Interestingly Titanium was discovered here.

Antiques, pictures and plates adorn the rooms and the use of beautiful fabrics around the home is testament to Annabel's background as an interior designer. A private staircase leads to the two guests rooms, between which is a guest sitting room replete with reading material and guides of the local area and sitting here awhile in front of the warming fire is an utter delight. Each guest bedroom has an en suite bathroom amply supplied with potions and lotions with which to indulge.

The gardens are tranquil with a walled garden and many specimen trees, shrubs and ponds. A choice of continental or traditional breakfast is offered and a fine array of local restaurants and pubs cater for all tastes for dinner. All in all, Creed House is the perfect Wolsey Lodge and you will be made to feel most welcome in a beautiful home.

The Hosts

Annabel and Jonathon took over the house from his parents who moved into a house in the grounds. Annabel now devotes her time to looking after her children, home, garden and guests whilst Jonathon works in nearby Truro as a stockbroker. They both enjoy travel and history when time allows.

The Location

In the heart of Cornwall, Creed House is 'local' to so much – the coast is under five miles away, Heligan, Eden, Trewithen, Caerhays, St Mawes, Trelissick, Truro, Padstow, St Ives, Penzance, Helford River, Minnack Theatre, Trerice House, Lanhydrock House and Pencarrow House to name just a few places to visit.

Finding Us

From Truro take A390 towards St Austell, after 7 miles you will reach Grampound. Half way up hill, just before the clock tower take right turn to Creed. After approx. 1 mile and just after the church left at the oak tree. The entrance to Creed House is second white gate on left.

Rooms (per person per night incl. breakfast)

1 Double Room	(en suite)	**£45**
1 Twin Room	(en suite)	**£45**

Meals

Breakfast only

Opening Times

Closed Christmas & New Year

Payment Options

Facilities & Services

John & Carla Caslin
Bay House
Housel Bay
The Lizard
Cornwall
TR12 7PG
Tel: 01326 290235 or 07740 168805
carla.caslin@btinternet.com
www.mostsoutherlypoint.co.uk 2956

The Property

As sensational locations go, Bay House may take some beating. Situated above Housel Bay on Cornwall's Lizard Peninsula, this stunning Wolsey Lodge occupies the most southerly location in England with miles of mesmerising ocean beyond. Just a short walk from the Lizard lighthouse, the garden drops down to the cliff footpath and direct access to the beach and many miles of coastal walking.

Bay House was built in the 1920s and the light, bright rooms take advantage of the dramatic coastline views and sea beyond. Antique and contemporary furniture complement the neutral shades of the décor whilst the soft furnishings reflect the bright, crisp colours of the house's surroundings. There are three extremely comfortable guest rooms, each with sea views. Ideal for relaxing and taking in the ever changing vista.

In the garden there are flowers normally native to far warmer climes but which happily thrive here due to its southerly, warmer location and the summer house and other seating areas are perfect on warmer days as somewhere to enjoy afternoon tea.

Breakfast is served in the open-plan dining area which has great views. Dinner too can be enjoyed, by arrangement, and of course fish is the local speciality. There are also local restaurants aplenty.

The Hosts

Carla and John moved to Bay House in 2010 having formerly run a B&B close by. Carla is Dutch and met John when he was working in Holland. John is now retired and is the resident 'cook'. They enjoy tennis, golf, art and painting.

The Location

As well as many National Trust gardens and houses in the vicinity, guests can also enjoy the Goonhilly Satellite Earth Station, the Museum of Submarine Telegraphy, Land's End, windsurfing in Coverack, The Lizard Peninsula, Sennen Cove, St. Michael's Mount, Lizard Lighthouse Heritage Centre, St Ives and Lizard Wireless Station.

Finding Us

From Helston take A3083 to The Lizard. In centre of Lizard village turn left - past row of houses on left and football pitch on right. After 500 yards take first turning right. Follow this road to very end, turn right onto short unmade road signed to Bay House. Turn left at green garage.

Rooms (per person per night incl. breakfast)

1 Double Room	(en suite)	from **£75**
1 Twin Room	(en suite)	from **£70**
1 Double Room	(private)	from **£65**

Meals

Supper	**£35**

Opening Times

Closed Christmas

Payment Options

Facilities & Services

David and Angela Carr
Sirelands,
Heads Nook, Brampton,
Cumbria CA8 9BT
Tel: 01228 670389
carr_sirelands@btconnect.com   **8975**

Finding Us

From M6 Junction 43 take A69 for Newcastle. After 3 miles turn right at traffic lights for Heads Nook (1½ miles). After village pass two junctions. Keep right at letter box, signposted Castle Carrock. 1 mile on, white house on left.

Rooms (per person per night incl. breakfast)

1 Double Room	(private)	**£45**
1 Twin Room	(en suite)	**£45**
Single Supplement		**£10**

Meals

Supper	**£22**
Dinner	**£27.50**

Opening Times

Closed Christmas & New Year

Payment Options

Facilities & Services

The Property

In this quiet, unsung corner of Cumbria, you will find Sirelands, a beautiful, sheltered and peaceful Cumbrian cottage overlooking the North Pennines, yet only ten minutes from the nearest M6 junction at Carlisle.

Guests are welcomed into this relaxing home with home baked afternoon tea, served in front of the open fire or in the summerhouse, depending on the season. Settle into a comfortable sofa in the large, traditionally decorated drawing room overlooking the garden. Throughout the house is a wealth of browsing material and bedtime reading for bookworms to enjoy.

Charming guest rooms, overlooking the garden, include a twin with extra long beds and a double with traditional style sleigh bed, offering tea and coffee making facilities and television. Both bathrooms, one en suite, the other a few steps from the double room have baths with showers over.

A secluded garden with tranquil pond and stream is home to roe deer and a wide variety of birds including families of wild ducks, while beyond are woodland walks with impressive displays of bluebells and foxgloves to gladden the heart in spring and summer.

The Hosts

David and Angela have farmed here since 1962 and have derived enormous pleasure from developing Sirelands, which has evolved from a traditional gardener's cottage dating from about 1730. They enjoy country pursuits available in the area and entertaining guests has always been an essential and enjoyable part of their lives.

The Location

The Lake District and Hadrians Wall are particular attractions, but there is also golf, fishing, the RSPB Reserve at Geltsdale and regular meetings at Carlisle race course. The city of Carlisle has many historic interests of its own.

The Property

Original Victorian features greet guests on arrival as well as a warm welcome from hosts Gerry and Marion. Dating back to 1825, the manor house sits in ¾ of an acre of peaceful walled gardens with wide-reaching views across Ulverston and Morecambe Bay. Rich in Victorian style, including original fireplaces in each bedroom, and furnished with graceful antiques, guests have a private lounge and conservatory that benefit from the glorious sea views. Bedrooms are large and combine genuine antique beds with modern luxury mattresses and linen along with tea making facilities, televisions, DVD players, hairdryers and bathrobes to guarantee guest's absolute comfort.

The Hosts

Originally a teacher, Marion ran a restaurant and outside catering company before raising children took over and then managed the BAE VIP guest house which set the standards that were brought to St Mary's Mount. Together with Gerry, who is an engineer working in the oil and gas field, they ran a wine shop in Ulverston for many years and share a passion for food which is evident in the substantial breakfasts guests enjoy which include home-made jams and marmalades, plus eggs from their own hens. Both enjoy fell walking and share their knowledge to help their guests enjoy the beauty of the area to the full.

The Location

St Mary's Mount is in a quiet area of Ulverston, a pleasant market town on the edge of the Lake District National Park and one hour's drive from the Yorkshire Dales. Ulvertson is world-renowned for its many festivals that offer something for everyone and the many National Trust attractions, fell walking and lakes provide a varied and exciting holiday.

Gerry & Marion Bobbett
St Mary's Mount
Belmont, Ulverston
Cumbria LA12 7HD
Tel: 01229 583372 or 07734 849005
gerry.bobbett@virgin.net
www.stmarysmount.co.uk   8970

Finding Us

Take J36 from M6, follow A590 to Barrow, when reaching Ulverston at second roundabout turn right to town centre, follow road around to junction, turn very sharp right, follow road up around to left past church, follow road around to right, take first turning on left signed Hoad Monument. St Mary's Mount drive is on right.

Rooms (per person per night incl. breakfast)

2 Double Rooms	(en suite)	£40
1 Twin Room	(private)	£45
1 Single Room	(private)	£45
Single Occupancy		£50

Meals

Supper	£20
Dinner	£27.50

Opening Times

Closed Christmas & New Year

Payment Options

Facilities & Services

The Property

Johnby Hall is a great location from which to explore all that the Lake District has to offer. Steeped in history, the Elizabethan manor house started life around 1350 as a fortified pele tower and has belonged to the Howard family since 1783. It is now home to Henry and Anna Howard who welcome guests looking for a comfortable base from which to enjoy the surrounding area.

Located in a pretty cottage in the garden, the Studio is an open-plan suite offering superbly comfortable double or twin accommodation; an extra occasional bed in the sitting-room area makes this a great option for families with up to two children. (A cot is also available for babies.) Kelly is in a seventeenth-century wing of the house and offers twin or double arrangements, with its own delightful sitting room. Breakfast is taken in the stunning 'great hall' where the history of the house is evident all around you, from family coats of arms to antique oak furniture and carefully-preserved architectural features.

Guests are welcome to explore several acres of informal gardens and adjacent woodlands, which are full of wildlife including red squirrels and deer.

The Hosts

Henry and Anna are both part-time professional musicians – Henry is a tenor and Anna is a harpist and soprano. (Musical guests feel especially at home here, and can enjoy playing the pianos in the Studio and great hall.) Henry, Anna and their young family are dedicated to ensuring a warm and friendly welcome for their guests.

The Location

Johnby Hall is located near Penrith in Cumbria, with the Lake District National Park's fells, dales and lakes on the doorstep. Guests will enjoy the many tourist attractions such as lake steamers, historic houses, gardens, castles and the many events, craft fairs and festivals that take place locally throughout the year in this part of Cumbria.

Henry and Anna Howard
Johnby Hall
Penrith
Cumbria CA11 0UU
Tel: 017684 83257 or 017684 80247
bookings@johnbyhall.co.uk
www.johnbyhall.co.uk   8955

Finding Us

Leave M6 at Penrith, J40. Take A66 westbound towards Keswick. After couple of miles (and a little after Rheged roundabout) take right exit marked Greystoke. At next T junction turn left to Greystoke (B5288). At Greystoke village green turn right to Johnby, taking left fork at Cycle Cafe. Johnby Hall is on left with white gates after a mile.

Rooms (per person per night incl. breakfast)

2 Suites	(en suite)	**£55-£62.50**
Single Supplement		**£25-£27.50**

Meals

Supper –	**£20**
by prior arrangement	

Opening Times

Open all year

Payment Options

Facilities & Services

David & Suzie Balfour
Morland House
Morland, Penrith, Cumbria CA10 3AZ
Tel: 01931 714989
enquiries@morlandhouse.net
www.morlandhouse.net   8959

Finding Us

Travelling North on M6: Turn off J39, approx 1½ miles north of Shap right turn to Newby/Morland. In Morland bear right down hill to 'The Square'. Crown Inn on right, Morland House gate on left as you enter the 'Square'. Travelling South on M6: Turn off J40 (Penrith) and take A66 East (Scotch Corner) for 1 mile to Roundabout. Turn south on A6 (towards Kendal/Shap) for 1 mile and left turn to Morland/Cliburn. In Cliburn right turn to Morland 1½ miles. In Morland bear left down hill into 'The Square' at the bottom. Crown Inn on right with Morland House gate on left as you enter 'The Square'.

Rooms (per person per night incl. breakfast)

1 Double Room	(private)	**£50-£70**
1 Double Room	(en suite)	**£50-£70**
1 Twin Room	(en suite)	**£50-£70**
Single Supplement		**£15**

Meals

Supper (24 hours notice required)   **£25**

Opening Times

May be closed during the winter

Payment Options

Facilities & Services

The Property

This fascinating Grade II listed building is mainly Victorian in character but parts of it go back to Tudor times. It has a wonderfully eccentric and intriguing feel with varying floor levels, small flights of steps and carved dark oak panelling. Originally a Vicarage, the family has lived here since 1828 and the house is brimming with history and with beautiful furniture and artefacts that all add to its attraction.

The impressive inner hall, with oriental rugs and wood burning stove, is used as the winter sitting room, whilst in the summer guests can enjoy the delights of the Drawing Room which opens onto the Rose Garden, a secluded haven on sunny afternoons. The bedrooms are spacious, beautifully decorated and furnished with antiques, comfortable seating, tea trays and televisions, and all have either en suite or private bathrooms. (The Garden Sitting Room and the Oak Bedroom can also be taken together to create a family suite).

The four acre gardens are charming, with lawns, yew walks, flower borders, a croquet lawn and Morland Beck flowing through which can be crossed either by bridge or stepping stones to the Quarry Garden or the Orchard.

The Hosts

David used to work in Finance and Marketing for British Coal. Suzie ran her own business before working as the Administrator for Eden Mind charity. Both now concentrate on looking after their bed and breakfast guests. They are keen golfers and enjoy skiing and motorcycling, and David bowls at county level.

The Location

Morland is 8 miles south of Penrith in Cumbria, just outside the Lake District National Park and perfectly located for exploring the Eastern and Northern Lakes. The beautiful, under-explored Eden Valley is one of England's best kept secrets with pretty walks and cycle routes. The Pennines, Yorkshire Dales and Hadrian's Wall are within easy reach.

The Property

Cook House is situated in the historic Cumbrian village of Levens overlooking Morecambe Bay and the Kent estuary, which together form a dramatically changing backdrop to this most beautiful home. As its name implies, the house was formerly a cook house for weary travellers making their way across the valley. Charmingly typical of this beautiful area, Cook House is perfectly located for exploring the Southern lakes as well as a convenient stop off on the way to Scotland.

You'll be welcomed on arrival with afternoon tea in the conservatory, garden terrace or when the weather is inclement, beside a cosy fire in the drawing room. Lucy has made this house into a most comfortable home that is light and sunny and furnished with fine art, furniture and family photographs.

The bedrooms are very comfortable and offer every luxury for guests, one has an adjoining spacious modern bathroom, the other an en suite . Both overlook a rose and box garden, which is just one part of the pretty gardens surrounding Cook House, all of which have been designed by Lucy.

The Hosts

Lucy grew up in the nearby family home of Levens Hall which is now owned by her brother. Generations of talented family artists precede Lucy and she herself is a talented water-colourist, professional photographer and flower arranger and is locally recognised for her garden designing.

The Location

Levens is a pretty village just 4 miles from Kendal. Close by and open to the visitors is the Elizabethan family home of Levens Hall with its worldwide famous topiary garden. Sizergh Castle, Holker Hall and Leighton Hall are all close by. The damson blossom in the Lyth Valley in Spring is worth a visit, and of course the delights of the Lake District are on the doorstep.

Mrs Lucy Sclater
Cook House
Church Road
Levens, Kendal
Cumbria LA8 8PU
Tel: 01539 561425
lucy@sclater.co.uk
www.sclater.co.uk　　　　8958

Finding Us

M6 Junction 36. A590 dual carriageway to Kendal/The Lakes, 1st turn signed Barrow/The Lakes. Dual Carriageway for 1 mile take right turn signed Brigsteer & Levens Village. Right again in front of Hare & Hounds pub into Church Road. At top of hill are 2 signs for school & 20mph on right hand side, straight after signs is Cook House, name is on gate.

Rooms (per person per night incl. breakfast)

1 Double Room	(private)	**£48**
1 Twin Room	(en suite)	**£48**

10% discount for 3 nights or more
15% discount for 5 nights or more

Meals

Supper	**£24**
Dinner	**£30**

Opening Times

Closed Christmas & New Year

Payment Options

Facilities & Services

The Property

A 14th century study, where guests can snuggle up to a roaring log fire, and a wonderfully romantic 16th century dining room, are just two of the secrets revealed when you step inside what is, from its exterior, a seemingly typical Victorian rectory.

There is a unique warmth and sense of serenity in this lovely home which was the runner up in the Enjoy England for Excellence awards Bed & Breakfast of the year 2008-2009. Beautifully decorated guest rooms have king size beds or larger and include thoughtful touches such as luxurious towelling dressing gowns, CD players and complimentary tea trays. There is every comfort and guests are also welcome to use the television and DVD in one of the two guest lounges.

Pre-dinner drinks are served in the drawing room or out on the terrace in the summer months with spectacular views of the purple tinged lakeside fells and mountains. Dining by candlelight in the intimate dining room enhances what is certainly one of the highlights of your stay.

The Hosts

Gill, a qualified home economist, is happy to cater for any dietary requirements. She is passionate about the quality and sourcing of ingredients favouring local, organic and Fair Trade produce. David also offers an international selection of fine wines, which are his special interest. There are over thirty wines to choose from, starting from £13 a bottle. Attention to detail, excellent personal service and generous hospitality are the watchwords here.

The Location

Situated in the quieter Northern Lakes, just 20 minutes drive from Keswick and the M6, this is the perfect setting from which to explore Buttermere, Derwent and Ullswater and the majestic peaks of Skiddaw and Blencathra.

Gill & David Taylor
Boltongate Old Rectory,
Near Ireby, Cumbria CA7 1DA
Tel: 01697 371647
boltongate@talk21.com
www.boltongateoldrectory.com 8979

Finding Us

South: M6 exit 41. B5305 to Wigton, at A595, left. After 5 miles left for Boltongate. Left at T-junction. In village follow for Ireby, down hill, driveway on left. North: A595 from Carlisle for 16 miles. Left for Boltongate, then as from south.

Rooms (per person per night incl. breakfast)

1 Double	(en suite)	£65
1 Double/Twin	(en suite)	£62.50
Single Supplement		£110-£115

Meals

Local Platter	£15
Dinner	£35

Opening Times

Closed December and January

Payment Options

Facilities & Services

Photograph: Clive Boursnell ©

Noel and Christy Page-Turner
Woodhayes,
Honiton, Devon EX14 4TP
Tel: 01404 42011
Fax: 01404 42011
cmpt@inweb.co.uk
www.woodhayes.co.uk   **2997**

Finding Us

Woodhayes is situated 1½ miles north east of Honiton. Take Dunkeswell road out of Honiton, cross small bridge over River Otter. 150 yards turn right. Woodhayes is first drive on left.

Rooms (per person per night incl. breakfast)

1 Single Room	(private)	**£46**
1 Double Room	(en suite)	**£48**
1 Twin Room	(en suite)	**£48**
Single occupancy of double or twin		**£56**

Meals

Dinner	**£30**

Opening Times

Closed occasionally

Payment Options

Facilities & Services

The Property

Proudly overlooking the Otter Valley and Honiton, in what Daniel Defoe once called "the finest landscape in the world", rises Woodhayes, an elegant listed Georgian farmhouse.

Dating back to the 14th century, Woodhayes is steeped in history and has a fascinating literary connection. Noel's Page-Turner ancestor was great aunt to one of Britain's greatest ever writers, Jane Austen, who often frequented nearby Lyme Regis.

The antique furniture, luxurious beds with fine bed linen and walls adorned with original paintings (including full length family portraits) make this an impressive, yet comfortable home from home.

Guests are encouraged to explore the one and a half acre garden and scenic walks on the farm in this designated Area of Outstanding Natural Beauty. Local attractions such as Dumpdon Hill, a Celtic hill fort and Luppitt Church are also worth a visit.

The Hosts

Christy and Noel are passionate about good food and they delight in sharing delicious four course meals, featuring the finest home grown vegetables and local meat and fish, with their guests. Active members of the local community, they clearly enjoy entertaining and meeting people from all walks of life. Noel can often be found mowing, planting trees, pruning the topiary and he also spends a lot of time involved with voluntary organisations.

The Location

The Jurassic Coast (including the fossil hunter's paradise of Lyme Regis), East Devon and Dorset are on the doorstep as is Honiton, the 'antique capital' of the South West with its bi-annual arts and music festival and the world's premier collection of Honiton lace.

Gail Sparkes
West Farm,
Irsha Street, Appledore, Nr Bideford,
Devon EX39 1RY
Tel: 01237 425269
westfarm@appledore-devon.co.uk
www.appledore-devon.co.uk   2993

The Property

West Farm, 400 years old and Grade II listed, is located in the village of Appledore with its long history of seafarers, smugglers and shipbuilding. Situated on Appledore's most picturesque street and just twenty paces from the sea, West Farm, which stands side-on to the road, appears to be, at first glance a small townhouse but upon entering its courtyard through the wrought iron gate you discover a grand unpretentious old home.

Of the three bedrooms the large Garden Suite with its direct access onto the beautiful and secluded secret garden is particularly popular. Devotees of antiques and high-ceilinged rooms opt for the spacious and traditionally decorated double room with its grand half-tester bed.

The Hosts

Gail and Peter encourage guests to make themselves at home; their generous, warm hospitality and the happy, relaxed atmosphere are of local renown. They will be happy to recommend several good pubs and restaurants in Appledore and Westward Ho!

The Location

As well as the local area, there are many delightful places to visit within an easy drive including, to the east, Exmoor, Lynton, and Lynmouth and, to the west, Bucks Mill, Clovelly and Hartland. RHS Rosemoor, Docton Mill and Marwood gardens are all within $\frac{1}{2}$ hours drive. Walkers can enjoy the North Devon coast path (all the way to Land's End if you they feel so inspired; Gail's outstanding breakfast will keep you going all day). The Royal North Devon Golf Club is just 1 mile away.

Finding Us

From junction 27, on the M5, take the A361 to Barnstable, then A39 to Bideford. After crossing the river (big bridge) turn right at the big roundabout and follow signs to Appledore. After St. Mary's Church, on the left, turn right into Irsha Street. West Farm is opposite the Royal George pub. Gail will direct you to off-road parking behind West Farm with direct access into the garden.

Rooms (per person per night incl. breakfast)

1 Double Room	(en suite)	**£50**
1 Twin Room	(en suite)	**£50**
1 Twin Room	(private)	**£47**
Single Supplement		**£10-£15**

Meals

Breakfast only

Opening Times

Closed Christmas & New Year

Payment Options

Facilities & Services

David & Helen Littlefair
Stoke Gabriel Lodgings
Badgers Retreat
2 Orchard Close
Paignton Road
Stoke Gabriel
Totnes
Devon TQ9 6SX
Tel: 01803 782003 or 07785 710225
Fax: 01803 782003
info@stokegabriellodgings.com
www.stokegabriellodgings.com   2959

Finding Us
Detailed instructions available at time of booking.

Rooms (per person per night incl. breakfast)

2 Double Rooms (en suite)	**£45-£50**
1 Double/Twin Room (en suite)	**£45-£50**
Single Supplement	**£15**

Meals
Breakfast Only

Opening Times
Closed Christmas

Payment Options

Facilities & Services

The Property

Stunning modern architecture, bright open living spaces and incredible views are the hallmarks of Stoke Gabriel Lodgings. Set high above the River Dart just outside the quintessentially English village of Stoke Gabriel, the house was completed in 2010 and has been designed to take full advantage of its elevated location deep in the Devon countryside.

On arrival you will be warmly greeted by your hosts David and Helen and offered a classic Devon cream tea and a chance to take in your rather special surroundings. The guest rooms are spacious and luxuriously furnished with comfortable seating areas, televisions and delicious offerings on tea trays. The en suite bathrooms are equally well thought out and designed complete with wet shower areas and heated towel rails for added comfort. Patio doors open to your own private balcony overlooking the garden – a perfectly quiet retreat to enjoy the peaceful location.

Oak floors, and furniture of the guest living and dining rooms reflect the contemporary light and airy ambience whilst outside the newly planted garden landscape is best enjoyed from the large terrace or conservatory. Breakfast offers an array of cooked delights whilst dinner can be taken at one of the many excellent local pubs and restaurants.

The Hosts

As hoteliers for over 30 years, David and Helen Littlefair know exactly what their guests expect and, together with their three grown-up daughters have created a lovely family home to share. Holidaying in Stoke Gabriel for many years before building a home here, their intimate knowledge of the best places to visit are eagerly shared with their guests.

The Location

National Trust and English Heritage properties as well as the South Devon Coastal Path, beaches galore and the diversely interesting towns of Brixham, Dartmouth, Totnes, Paignton and Torquay are all within reach. Above all take in the wild open splendour of Dartmoor for walking and cycling.

Sue & Guy Sherratt
Bracken House
Bratton Fleming
Barnstaple
Devon EX31 4TG
Tel: 01598 711810
info@brackenhouse.co.uk
www.brackenhouse.co.uk   2961

Finding Us

From South Molton, take A399 towards Ilfracombe; continue on road past Brayford continue until left turning towards Bratton Fleming. Bear left into village. Downhill for 500 yards and, opposite Post Office, turn left down drive with a sign at the end and follow signs down to the house.

Rooms (per person per night incl. breakfast)

2 Double Rooms (en suite)	**£45-£50**
1 Twin/Double Room (en suite)	**£45-£50**
Single Supplement	**£15**

Meals

Supper (By prior arrangement)	**£15**

Opening Times

Open all year

Payment Options

Facilities & Services

The Property

A short distance from the centre of the pretty Devon village of Bratton Fleming, amidst seven acres of gardens is the old rectory known as Bracken House. Home to Sue and Guy Sherratt, and their two children since 2009 it is now a welcoming family home. Antiques and art sit comfortably alongside relaxed furnishings and the library is packed with interesting books. A Devon cream tea on arrival is served in the library or on fine days outside on the plant-filled terrace.

Bracken House was once home to Reverend Wodehouse, uncle of PG Wodehouse who is known to have stayed here, perhaps drawing inspiration for some of his colourful characters. The guest rooms are suitably named 'Jeeves, 'Wooster' and 'Anatole'. 'Jeeves' has a double bed, 'Wooster' can be either a twin or a double and 'Anatole' is the 4'6" double on the ground floor and all three have en suite bathrooms furnished with the finishing touches you would expect. Delicious breakfasts, and a supper if you choose, feature local produce and seasonal offerings from the garden.

Outside the wonderful views across the surrounding countryside extend across Devon and on clear days to the sea and across to Appledore and Hartland Point.

The Hosts

Sue is a professional harpist and when not gardening, riding or looking after her guests, finds time to play concerts and teach. Guy is a chartered surveyor with his own estate agency with properties in France, Spain and Portugal. In his spare time he enjoys cooking and gardening.

The Location

Bracken House is located in Bratton Fleming, near Barnstaple in Devon and is the perfect base for exploring all of Exmoor and Devon with their many varied beaches, pretty villages and towns such as Croyde, Dunster, Barnstaple, South Molton and Ilfracombe. Lundy Island and Woolacombe Bay are all within reach and easy access to A361 takes you down into Cornwall too.

Graham & Nichola Hawkins
Kerswell Farmhouse
Cornworthy, Totnes, Devon TQ9 7HH
Tel: 01803 732013 or 07584 578880
gjnhawkins@rocketmail.com
www.kerswellfarmhouse.co.uk   **2955**

Finding Us

From M5/A38 to Plymouth - Exit Dart Bridge
Junction A384 to Totnes - At roundabout
in Dartington left A385 - At lights in Totnes
right A381 to Kingsbridge - At top of hill
left to Ashprington - At first crossroads left
between pillars - At second crossroads right
to Bow Bridge, follow road to Tuckenhay -
At T-junction follow road left - At top of hill
right to Tideford and Dartmouth - Kerswell
Farmhouse is on the right after Furze Cross.

The Property

Could this be the B&B holiday location? Personally guided
tours of Dartmoor; staying in a divinely Devon Longhouse in
a secluded setting overlooking the surrounding hills; dining
on some of the finest fare to be found locally and looked after
by truly kind and caring hosts – what more could you ask for?

Kerswell Farmhouse is located just outside the village of
Cornworthy near the River Dart, the original farmhouse
dating back over 400 years. Additions and refurbishment
mean that it now offers all the modern-day luxuries for
a highly comfortable stay. There are five well-appointed
bedrooms, three in the main house and two in the adjacent
barn conversion. A further single room is available for
friends or a family group. Each room has under floor
heating, sumptuous pocket-sprung mattresses and goose
down duvets and is individually styled and furnished with
finishing touches including fresh flowers, well-stocked tea
tray and White Company toiletries.

Downstairs is highly comfortable, airy and light with a
plentiful supply of reading materials including local maps
and guides to help you make the most of your stay. Dining
here is equally delightful with finely prepared seasonal and
local produce being the hallmarks of every meal.

The Hosts

Graham and Nichola Hawkins are behind your welcome
when you arrive. Graham ran an international school in
Kuwait for 17 years and Nichola was an interior designer
before they returned to Devon. Nichola is a most
accomplished cook with a fine repertoire of dishes featuring
local Devon fayre to tempt her guests.

The Location

The gardens and grounds around Kerswell Farmhouse may
make you reluctant to step further afield, however Dartmoor
is on your doorstep and close by there is the South Devon
Coast Path, South Hams AONB, Dartmouth with its lovely
harbour, the ancient town of Totnes and Ashburton with its
antiques centre as well as Blue Flag beaches, steam railway,
historic houses, castles and gardens aplenty and within reach.

Rooms   (per person per night incl. breakfast)

1 Super King Size Double Room (en suite)	**£65**
2 King Size Double Rooms (en suite)	**£50 & £55**
1 Twin/Super King Size Double Room (en suite)	**£55**
1 Single Room (private)	**£60**
Single Occupancy – 20% less than room rate	

Meals

Dinner (By prior arrangement)	**£30**

Opening Times

Closed December and New Year's Day

Payment Options

Facilities & Services

John & Fleur Hoare
Huish Manor,
Winterborne Zelston, Blandford Forum,
Dorset DT11 9ES
Tel: 01929 459065
hoare@huish.fsnet.co.uk   **1995**

Finding Us

Travelling West on A31, past Wimborne, there is a 2 mile long brick wall on the left. At the end of this, and 50 yards past the Worlds End public house, there is a sign 'Huish only' indicating a slip road to the right, leading to the drive of the house. This is before the turning to Winterborne Zelston.

The Property

This very pretty, Grade II listed house, built in 1792, is approached along an attractive tree lined drive and is fronted by a large lawn with a pretty walled garden at the back and an adjoining small wood, orchard, and paddocks.

The house has attractive well proportioned rooms as befits a house of this period. The drawing room and dining room are available for guests' use and are furnished with antiques and a fine collection of marine paintings. The dining room is particularly elegant with a log fire, lit when appropriate, at both dinner and breakfast.

The bedrooms are large and comfortable, with antique furniture and beds made up with linen sheets and warm blankets. Each has its own bathroom, one with a power shower, and enjoy calming views either onto the front lawn, or the walled garden at the back.

The Hosts

John worked in the City of London until retiring. He is a keen sailor. Fleur trained as a dancer and, until recently, taught children ballet. Fleur is an excellent cook and they both greatly enjoy entertaining guests in the surroundings of their attractive 18th century house.

The Location

The house is ideally situated for visiting Hardy Country including Dorchester, Blandford Forum, Wimborne, Studland Bay, and Poole. There are a number of interesting museums, beautiful houses such as Kingston Lacy and castles at Corfe and Lulworth. For those who enjoy walking, there is the lovely Dorset coastline, recently declared a World Heritage Site. Other attractions include the famous Dorset Steam Fair in August.

Rooms (per person per night incl. breakfast)

1 Double Room	(private)	£45-£55
1 Twin Room	(private)	£45-£55
Single Supplement		£10

Meals

Dinner	£26

Opening Times

Closed Christmas, New Year & Easter

Payment Options

Facilities & Services

Peter & Cari Sorby
Manor Barn
Upper Street,
Child Okeford,
Blandford Forum,
Dorset DT11 8EF
Tel: 01258 860638 or 07973 595344
carisorby@btinternet.com   **1986**
www.manorbarnbedandbreakfast.co.uk

The Property

Let's set the scene for a real treat; an old red brick and stone house, an area of outstanding natural beauty and a very caring hostess. Manor Barn offers all this ~ and more!

This beautifully converted barn has its own entrance into a sitting room with a private dining area and two very stylish ground floor, oak beamed bedrooms each with a stunning en suite bathroom. Cari is a wonderful hostess, offering tea and homemade cakes on arrival and the sort of breakfast that sets one up for a day spent exploring this lovely area, all produced using mostly local ingredients.

The ground floor bedrooms are ideal for less able guests and Cari excels at making sure their needs are met. From the front of the house is a spectacular view of Hambledon Hill and by following the footpath from the end of the drive to the top of the hill you will be rewarded with amazing views over five counties and the knowledge that you have achieved a climb of some 603 feet and therefore thoroughly deserve to relax in luxury on your return.

The Hosts

Cari and Peter are welcoming and charming hosts who look after guests as if they are old friends. Peter works in nearby Sherborne whilst Cari looks after the house, their two sons, and the family's dogs. They both love this area of Dorset and sharing their favourite places with guests.

The Location

Dorset is a wonderful county, boasting glorious coastline, beautiful countryside, pretty villages and market towns and some of the most archaeologically important sites in the country along the Jurassic coast. Sherborne with its castle and Abbey is close by and there are magnificent houses and gardens at Kingston Lacy, Athelhampton House, Longleat and Stourhead within easy reach.

Finding Us

Heading south on A350 from Shaftesbury, turn right at the sign 'Child Okeford 3 miles'. Nearly 3 miles later Manor Barn drive is on the left immediately in front of a 20mph road sign

Rooms   (per person per night incl. breakfast)

2 Double/Twin Rooms (en suite)	**£50**
Single Supplement	**£25**

Meals

Dinner (excl. Sun)	**£25-£40**
By prior arrangement	

Opening Times

Open all year

Payment Options

Facilities & Services

Hugh and Miranda Sutton
The Old Rectory
Pimperne
Dorset DT11 8UB
Tel: 01258 451555
the_old_rectory@hotmail.co.uk　　**1980**

The Property

Many Wolsey Lodges have fascinating histories dating back many hundreds of years and The Old Rectory is no exception. Rebuilt in 1704 following a fire, the original house was a hunting lodge owned by Henry VIII and home to Catherine Parr. Original Tudor features are apparent and blend with the new to create a beautiful family home with a welcoming atmosphere set amidst lovingly restored gardens.

A wide hallway leads into the drawing room where guests can relax with a good book or take a turn on the baby grand piano before perhaps exploring the three acres of garden with their manicured lawns, ha-ha, abundantly flowering beds, shady trees and a tennis court for the more energetic.

There are two bedrooms available to guests, a double with en suite bathroom and a twin on the second floor with a private bathroom. Both are beautifully decorated as Miranda was an interior designer before moving to Dorset and has brought all her skill to bear to ensure her guests complete comfort. She is also a Cordon Bleu chef preparing delicious breakfasts and, when requested, will serve a dinner that will delight you.

The Hosts

Hugh and Miranda Sutton moved to Dorset from London and the worlds of publishing and interior design. The welcoming, peaceful retreat they have created reflects their personal taste in fine furnishings and art and together they work hard to ensure that their guests have a memorable stay.

The Location

The Old Rectory is in the heart of the village of Pimperne located close to the preserved Georgian splendour of Blandford Forum and within reach of Stonehenge and Salisbury Cathedral. Close by is the thatched village of Milton Abbas whilst slightly further afield are Stourhead, Thomas Hardy's house and the famous and stunning Jurassic coastline. It is also well placed for a visit to Kingston Lacy, the National Trust house at Wimborne Minster. There is so much to see and do in Dorset you'll be spoilt for choice.

Finding Us

From Blandford take A354 Salisbury Road. After 1 mile Pimperne is on left. Turn left into Church Road (the Farquharson pub is on right), follow Church Road to a high wall on left with double green gates marked The Old Rectory.

Rooms (per person per night incl. breakfast)

1 Double Room (en suite)		£67.50
1 Twin Room (private)		£55
Single Supplement		£15

Meals

Supper	£25
Dinner	£35
(Both by prior arrangement)	

Opening Times

Closed Christmas & New Year

Payment Options

Facilities & Services

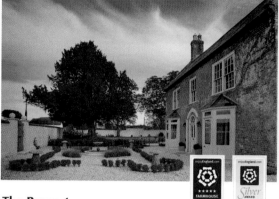

The Property

This stunning Georgian farmhouse offers guests luxurious comfort and supreme hospitality in a breathtaking setting.

Your arrival will be marked with delicious tea and cakes in front of a fire in the drawing room or, when the weather permits, a sunny corner of Launceston Farm's beautiful walled garden. This house has a most calming ambience and all six en suite bedrooms have an air of lavish comfort with ornate, antique furniture and slipper baths in three rooms. Wireless internet access is available throughout the house. Guests are welcome to explore the 800 acre organic farm and enjoy the outdoor swimming pool in summer.

Much of the food served here has been grown on the farm and the menu, should you request dinner as well as breakfast, will feature delicious cordon bleu cooking at its very best.

The Hosts

Your hostess is Sarah Worrall who runs the farm with her family. Sarah's enthusiasm and love of her home and the countryside around her is evident and she happily shares this with her guests. From the welcome you receive on arrival to the detailed information compiled about the best places to visit in Dorset, Sarah will ensure your stay here is very special indeed.

The Location

Stunning coasts and undulating countryside are the hallmarks of Dorset. Historic towns such as Wimborne and Salisbury vie for attention alongside the natural wonders of Poole Harbour and the Jurassic Coast whilst for history lovers there is the preserved 18thC Milton Abbas village and Bovington Tank Museum. Nature lovers should not miss a visit to Abbotsbury Swannery or Monkey World.

Sarah Worrall
Launceston Farm
Tarrant Launceston
Blandford
Dorset DT11 8BY
Tel: 01258 830528
info@launcestonfarm.co.uk
www.launcestonfarm.co.uk   1981

Finding Us

From the A354 Salisbury to Blandford road, turn left at Tarrant Hinton, Tarrant Launceston is the first village and the house entrance is signed on the right just passed the farm entrance.

Rooms (per person per night incl. breakfast)

2 Double Rooms (en suite)	£45-£50
2 Superior Double Rooms (en suite)	£52.50-£57.50
2 Superior Double/ Twin Rooms (en suite)	£52.50-£57.50
Single Occupancy	£65-£115

Meals

Supper	£22.50

Opening Times

Open all year

Payment Options

Facilities & Services

The Property

Arriving in Ashmore on a fine day one is able to appreciate just how high you've climbed with views across to the Dorset coast and the Isle of Wight over 30 miles away. Tear yourself away for tea and home baked cakes at Glebe Farm which is situated in the heart of the village. Built in 2004 and designed to take advantage of the magnificent views all around as well as the complete and utter tranquillity of this quiet slice of Dorset. Inside, glass walls create a light and spacious feel and the central dining hall with its completely glazed wall allows uninterrupted views across the fields beyond.

The bedrooms, located to the side of the house, are beautifully furnished with armchairs and table, well-stocked hospitality tray, fresh flowers, television, iPod docks and internet access. The upstairs room has a Juliette balcony whilst downstairs French doors lead on to a private deck to make the most of the views.

A light supper is offered for guests in their room if they choose or guests can enjoy a full dinner in the dining room or candlelit terrace. Whichever option is chosen, enjoy local fare supplemented by homemade produce all cooked to perfection and enjoyed in the most wonderful setting.

The Hosts

Tessa and Ian Millard oversaw the building of the house themselves before moving in from their farmhouse next door. They have three grown up children and run a large arable, sheep and beef farm. Dogs and horses are family favourites here and Tessa enjoys the additional challenge of side-saddle on one of her horses.

The Location

Ashmore has a dewpond dating back to Roman times which is not to be missed; neither are the many walks emanating from the village. Stonehenge, Shaftesbury, Salisbury, Stourhead House, Abbotsbury Swannery and the Jurassic coast are all within reach.

Tessa & Ian Millard
Glebe Farm
Ashmore
Shaftesbury
Dorset SP5 5AE
Tel: 01747 811974 or 07799858961
tmillard@glebe.f9.co.uk
www.glebefarmbandb.co.uk   1977

Finding Us

From Shaftesbury take A30 towards Salisbury. After 3 miles enter Ludwell. At top of hill turn right (signed Ashmore) follow road to top of hill. Left at crossroads. After 200yds turn right, follow road into Ashmore. Pass pond in centre of village. Just past memorial on right is Glebe Farm sign.

Rooms (per person per night incl. breakfast)

2 Super King Double Rooms (en suite)	£50-£60
Single Supplement	£20

Meals

Supper	£15
Dinner	£25
(Both by prior arrangement)	

Opening Times

Closed Christmas & New Year

Payment Options

£ C

Facilities & Services

BYO | 14 | ☀ | PETS | ⌂ | ✓ | WiFi | ♨

The Property

Staying on what is arguably one of the country's finest fishing and shooting estates is of course a treat for any sportsman. Combine this with a fine Georgian country house offering exceptionally luxurious B&B hospitality and you have a location anyone would be happy to visit.

The Wrackleford Estate has been in the Pope family for six generations and is now home to Katie and Oliver and their three children. Set in the heart of the Frome Valley in Dorset, everything here is gloriously and quintessentially English and the house is a classic reflection of this with antique furnishing, family photos and paintings, whilst outside the sweeping lawns lead down to the River Wrackle and beyond are meadows and a waterfall. A welcoming tea on arrival is enjoyed in the plant-filled conservatory whilst a sunny spot outside is the perfect location for a lazy breakfast.

Each guest room is large and comfortable with bathrooms that feature marble bath and basin surrounds and feel, quite simply, luxuriously decadent. Breakfast is an excellent affair of local produce and Katie will pack you a sumptuous picnic lunch or offer to cook a barbecue on the river banks if you're fishing. Dinner can be enjoyed at any of the excellent local restaurants. Bicycles are available on request.

The Hosts

Wrackleford is Oliver's family home but he spent time in the army before moving here with his young family in 2006. A keen interest in the countryside makes both he and Katie natural guardians of this wonderful estate and they enthusiastically and warmly welcome their B&B guests to enjoy all it has to offer with them.

The Location

Aside from the estate fishing and shooting, this area of Dorset has much to offer visitors. The Thomas Hardy and Tutankhamun museums, Maiden Castle, Cerne Abbas Giant, Corfe and Sherborne Castles, Longleat and the wild Jurassic coast are all within easy reach.

Katie Pope
Wrackleford House
Dorchester
Dorset DT2 9SN
Tel: 01305 264141
katie@wrackleford.co.uk
www.wrackleford.co.uk　　1976

Finding Us

Wrackleford House is set 2 miles north of the county town of Dorchester, close to the village of Stratton. Detailed directions available on request.

Rooms (per person per night incl. breakfast)

2 Double Rooms (en suite)		**£65**
2 Twin Rooms (en suite)		**£65**
Single Supplement		**£35**

Meals

Breakfast only

Opening Times

Closed Christmas & New Year

Payment Options

Facilities & Services

The Property

Overlooking the seafront in Old Harwich, Esplanade House is an impressively restored four storey Grade II listed former 'Captain's House' that enjoys panoramic views of the harbour entrance and the open sea beyond.

Welcomed by your hosts it is hard to feel anything less than totally at home here – the warmth of your surroundings is matched only by how much they so clearly love having guests stay with them.

The bedrooms face the waterfront and offer comfort and luxury. There are two main guest rooms, both are spacious and have a double bed, comfortable seating and television. One is on the second floor, the other is on the third floor and each has a private bathroom with under floor heating. There is also a third smaller twin-bed Attic room which, with one of the double bedrooms, makes up a family suite. Outside there is a small courtyard at the side of the house where guests can relax in the warmer weather and the promenade and beach are just a short stroll away. Exploring this fascinating town might include the High and Low lighthouses, Ha'Penny Pier and perhaps a visit to the oldest cinema in the country!

Making the most of local produce, breakfast, and dinner, if you eat in, is a treat whilst the abundance of high quality restaurants and pubs close by gives ample choice.

The Hosts

Your hosts are Martin, a boat surveyor and Liz, a psychotherapist. They have travelled extensively, yet retain a love for the charms of East Anglia. They enjoy sailing, walking, cooking, local history, natural history, antiques, literature and art. They have a grown up family of four.

The Location

Easy access to Constable Country, the oldest recorded town of Colchester, the Suffolk Heritage Coast of Woodbridge. Sutton Hoo, Orford, Aldeburgh and many other coastal towns and villages of East Anglia.

Martin & Liz Evans
Esplanade House
32 Kings Quay Street
Harwich
Essex CO12 3ES
Tel: 01255 508235 or 07887 724055
enquiries@esplanadehouse.co.uk
www.esplanadehouse.co.uk   3960

Finding Us

A120 to its termination on The Quay (passing Pier Hotel on right). Turn right into Kings Quay Street for 200m, veer left onto Wellington Road for 150m, turn right into Kings Quay Street again. Esplanade House is second house, private parking opposite. Full details sent on booking.

Rooms (per person per night incl. breakfast)

2 Double Rooms (private)	**£60**
Single Supplement	**£20**

Meals

Supper	**£20**
Dinner	**£30**

Opening Times

Closed occasionally

Payment Options

Facilities & Services

The Property

Promising a perfect escape from the turmoil of modern city life, Drakestone is a small estate in a beautiful and protected part of the Cotswolds. In a magnificent setting on the edge of beech woods, it is a fine example of an Arts & Crafts building, mentioned in Pevsner's 'The Cotswolds'.

Drakestone reveals an unusual blend of simplicity and originality - a house built by artists, for artists. The green panelled drawing room for guests leads from the entrance hall with its large oak door into the spacious dining room and through into a plant-filled conservatory. Upstairs, stained wood floors along a wide passage take you to the bedrooms, all with magnificent views over the gardens and the Vale of Berkeley.

Hugh's grandparents, influenced by painting trips to Italy and by the style of the period, laid out the gardens with tall yew hedges, informal walkways and a sunken pond. You can enjoy exploring its hidden corners.

The Hosts

Hugh and Crystal are informal hosts, providing a warm welcome in a house that is very much a home. They both have a varied background - ex British Council in West Africa, college lecturer, interior designer - and broad interests including arts and travel.

The Location

Badminton, Gatcombe, Cheltenham Races and Cheltenham Festivals of Literature and Music in spring and autumn; Bristol and Bath, Painswick Rococo Gardens, Slimbridge Wildfowl Trust, Westonbirt Arboretum, Berkeley Castle, Dyrham House, Newark Park, Owlpen Manor, golf, gliding and hill walking – there's an endless list of places to see and things to do.

Hugh & Crystal Mildmay
Drakestone House,
Stinchcombe, Dursley,
Gloucestershire GL11 6AS
Tel: 01453 542140
Fax: 01453 542140   **5998**

Finding Us

Northbound travellers leave M5 at exit 14, southbound travellers at exit 13. Drakestone is situated between Dursley (3 miles) and Wotton-under-Edge (3 miles) on B4060. House signposted from B4060.

Rooms (per person per night incl. breakfast)

2 Double Rooms (private)	**£44**
1 Twin Room (private)	**£44**
Single Occupancy	**£55**

Meals

Breakfast only

Opening Times

Closed December & January

Payment Options

Facilities & Services

The Property

Warm hospitality, excellent cooking and great peace is assured in this small Georgian Rectory, set in a Domesday listed village. Surrounded by ten acres of quiet garden and paddocks, with panoramic views over the Cotswold Hills, Winstone Glebe is the perfect rural retreat.

Tea awaits guests in the drawing room in front of a blazing log fire or, on fine days, in the garden. Comfortable, traditionally furnished guest rooms have classic furniture and floral fabrics, giving them a relaxed and romantic atmosphere. All rooms have large comfortable beds.

The garden, which includes a tennis court, was originally laid out by Dame Sylvia Crowe in the 1950s. Susanna has softened these rather austere bones with masses of spring bulbs and herbaceous planting, providing year round colour, from carpets of aconites in January, to Sedum - Autumn Joy - which retains its architectural beauty through to December.

The Hosts

Dinner is superbly prepared by Susanna, a professional cook who once ran the Cordon Bleu Restaurant. Shaun has lived in the Cotswolds all his life and is very familiar with the area.

The Location

Gardens abound in this beautiful region including Miserden, Rodmarton, Owlpen, Hidcote and Kiftsgate, and famous arboreta at Westonbirt and Batsford. Also there are lovely towns and villages such as Bibury, The Slaughters, Cirencester, Tetbury, Painswick, Stow and Chipping Campden, rich in antique shops, rural crafts and local history. Oxford, Bath and Stratford-upon-Avon are within easy reach. Being within an Area of Outstanding Natural Beauty there are numerous well signposted walks for the more energetic.

Shaun and Susanna Parsons
Winstone Glebe, Winstone,
Cirencester, Gloucestershire GL7 7LN
Tel: 01285 821451
sparsons@winstoneglebe.com
www.winstoneglebe.com   **5992**

Finding Us

15 minutes from the M5 junction 11a; 30 minutes from M4 junction 15. Follow signs to Cirencester in both cases. Winstone is 6 miles north west of Cirencester off the A417. Once in the village follow signs to church. The Glebe is just short of the church on the left on a bend by a public footpath sign.

Rooms (per person per night incl. breakfast)

1 Double/Twin Room (en suite)	**£45**
1 Twin Room (private)	**£45**
1 Double Room (private)	**£45**
Single Supplement	**£15**

Meals

Dinner (occasionally by prior arrangement)	**£30**

Opening Times

Closed occasionally

Payment Options

Facilities & Services

Jim & Susie Wilson
Westward,
Sudeley, Winchcombe,
Gloucestershire GL54 5JB
Tel: 01242 604372
Fax: 01242 609198
jimw@haldon.co.uk
www.westward-sudeley.co.uk   5989

The Property

The views from this beautiful Georgian Cotswold stone house, once visited by George III, are only revealed on arrival, across the lovely gardens to the lake and the far side of the glorious Sudeley valley. In this tranquil setting, the Wilsons delight in sharing their very English home.

The traditionally furnished drawing room and dining room are for guests' exclusive use. In winter, the drawing room has a roaring log fire, whilst in summer, these rooms open out onto the terrace and lovingly tended garden which comes to life in vibrant colour.

Three warm, comfortable bedrooms, each with en suite bath and thermostatic shower are furnished in distinctive period style. Hot water capacity is ample, having been specified with guests in mind! All beds are king size, whilst the Blue and Green rooms can be set up with two single 3 foot beds.

The Hosts

This is Jim's family home and he manages much of the estate and woodland whilst also working in London 2 to 3 days a week. Jim and Susie are widely travelled and lead a busy life with the farm and animals. Susie sculpts and trained at Prue Leith's School of Food and Wine and, although she hardly ever provides evening meals now, guests enjoy the extensive breakfast menu, including kedgeree and fishcakes, as well as delicious teas on arrival. Within one mile is Winchcombe, which boasts good places to eat across the price range, including that run by the Best Gloucestershire Chef (voted 2008) and a friendly gastro-pub; there is further choice within 3 to 4 miles.

The Location

Westward sits close to all the main Cotswold attractions - Broadway, Chipping Campden and Stow are all within 20 minutes, Stratford 40 minutes, Oxford and Warwick are 1 hour away and Bath 75 minutes. Hidcote and Kiftsgate are close by, as is Cheltenham, just 8 miles away, yet invisible behind the silhouette of Cleeve Hill.

Finding Us

In Winchcombe leave Abbey Square heading north on B4632, leaving Lloyds TSB Bank on your right. After 50m turn right into Castle Street. Follow this lane for approximately 1 mile. Past the farm buildings on the right turn right, signposted to Sudeley Lodge. Drive for approximately 800m, past 2 cottages until you arrive at the house.

Rooms (per person per night incl. breakfast)

3 Double Rooms (en suite)	**£45-£55**
Single Supplement	**£15**

Meals

Breakfast only

Opening Times

Closed 1st December-1st March

Payment Options

Facilities & Services

Robin & Sylvie Mills
Home Farm,
Little Barrington,
Burford,
Gloucestershire, OX18 4TQ
Tel: 01451 844300 or 07765 067887
sylviemills@yahoo.fr   **5957**

The Property
Mellow Cotswold stone, glorious gardens and the warmest of welcomes – the scene is set for an unforgettable experience. Robin and Sylvie are justifiably proud of their beautiful home which is part of the estate owned by Robin's family for the past two hundred years.

Sylvie's interior design background is evident in the inspired use of colour and family antiques, with large comfortable sofas in the sitting room to the more formal but elegant drawing room and dining room. The bedrooms (one with a spectacular four poster bed) and bathrooms are spacious and extremely comfortable and boast televisions, tea trays and luxurious selections of soaps, shampoos and lotions for pampering after a days sightseeing.

Sylvie is a superb cook and welcomes guests with tea and home made cakes on arrival, which can be followed by a delicious supper or dinner (often using wonderful smoked food from the Upton Smokery on the estate and which is run by Robin's son).

The Hosts
Robin and Sylvie are a charming, easy going couple. Robin is a retired businessman and has many interesting stories about the history of the estate, whilst Sylvie, who is French, has a background in interior design, and they both have a love of the countryside and outdoor pursuits.

The Location
On the eastern edge of the Cotswolds, equidistant between Cheltenham and Oxford this is the ideal base for touring the region. Whether your interest lies in the horse racing at Cheltenham, visiting picturesque Cotswold villages such as Burford and Bourton on the Water, magnificent Blenheim Palace, the Oxford Colleges or the Roman Villa at Chedworth, this area has so much to offer.

Finding Us
From Burford: Stay on A40 West. On next bend after 'Welcome to Gloucestershire' sign, turn right into drive to Home Farm. From Cheltenham: Follow A40 towards Burford. Pass the Inn of All Seasons and petrol station on left and pass sign to The Barringtons. Shortly after lodge on left is entrance to Home Farm. The house is down the drive on the right.

Rooms (per person per night incl. breakfast)

2 Double Rooms (en suite)	**£60-£65**
1 Twin Room (en suite)	**£60-£65**
Single Supplement	**£20**
Supplement for Cheltenham Festival may apply.	

Meals

Supper – 2 courses	**£25**
Dinner - 3 courses	**£30**

Opening Times
Closed Christmas, New Year & occasionally.

Payment Options

Facilities & Services

David and Jane Bruce
Willowside House & Farm
Withington
Cheltenham
Gloucestershire GL54 4DA
Tel: 01242 890557 or 07771 875648
info@willowside-estate.co.uk
www.willowside-estate.co.uk   5956

The Property
Overlooking 'Happy Valley' – what delights this conjures up – Willowside is a large quintessential Cotswold stone house in the lovely village of Withington, near the classic spa town of Cheltenham and market town of Cirencester with its Roman history. Recently renovated, this 17th century home is very comfortable with oak floors, antique furniture and beautiful furnishings that create a warm ambience reflecting the welcoming hosts, Jane and David Bruce.

The spacious well appointed bedrooms offer a relaxing retreat at the end of a busy day either exploring this beautiful area, or attending business meetings. Guests will enjoy the rolling Cotswold and village views. Each room is equipped with television, DVD, internet access and printing facilities. Breakfast and dinner, if requested, is prepared by Jane an accomplished cook, and served in either the formal dining room or the relaxed atmosphere of the large family kitchen.

Enjoy the landscaped gardens. Consider taking a walk to the River Colne. Through meadows to St Michael's Church and home via the Mill Inn.

The Hosts
Jane has run Willowside House & Farm as a B&B for many years. David is a retired company director. They have received excellent independent guest reviews.

The Location
The spa town of Cheltenham, famous for its racing, music, literary, jazz and science festivals is a short drive away. Spend a day at historic Stratford-up-Avon or simply meander through the Cotswolds visiting Stow-on-the-Wold, Chipping Campden, Broadway and other pretty villages. Business visitors enjoy easy access to Gloucester, Oxford, Swindon, Bristol, M4 and M5. For garden lovers, Chedworth Roman Villa, Barnsley, Kiftsgate and Hidcote, plus Westonbirt and Batsford arboreta are within easy reach.

Finding Us
Withington Village can be approached from Oxford (A40) - 40 miles; Cheltenham (A436) - 9 miles; Cirencester (A429) - 8 miles. The house is on the corner, adjacent to old farm buildings at the opposite end of the village to the church.

Rooms (per person per night incl. breakfast)
3 Double Rooms (en suite)	**£60**
Supplement for Cheltenham Festivals may apply.	
Single Occupancy	**£95**

(2 night stay preferred - 5% discount on 3 nights or more)

Meals
Supper	**£30**

Opening Times
Closed Christmas & New Year

Payment Options

Facilities & Services

Dr and Mrs J Ireland
Aylworth Manor
Aylworth, Naunton
Gloucestershire GL54 3AH
Tel: 01451 850850 or 07768 810357
enquiries@aylworthmanor.co.uk
www.aylworthmanor.co.uk   5948

Finding Us

From A40 at Northleach take A429 towards Bourton-on-the-Water, after 100 yards turn left signed Turkdean & Notgrove. Follow road for 3.9 miles to 'T' junction, turn right, take first left signed Aylworth. After ¾ mile entrance to drive is signed Aylworth Manor. If you start to go up other side of hill you have gone too far.

Rooms (per person per night incl. breakfast)

1 Double Room (en suite)	£50
1 Double/Twin (private)	£45
Single Supplement	£10

Meals

Supper	£25
Dinner	£30
(Both by prior arrangement)	

Opening Times

Open all year

Payment Options

£ € C TC VISA ⊖ Maestro

Facilities & Services

BYO °10 🏠 ✳ 🏃 👤 🛏 ✔ WiFi 🚭

The Property

Location, location, location. What a perfect place to find a Wolsey Lodge. Set in the heart of the glorious Cotswold hills you cannot help but appreciate the seclusion of Aylworth Manor and yet you are no more than 12 miles from the bustling, interesting heart of Cheltenham and less than an hour from Stratford-upon-Avon and Oxford.

Aylworth Manor is over 500 years old and has been carefully restored over the last few years by John and Joanna Ireland who together have turned it into a most friendly, welcoming family home for their two teenage children and the many guests that are lucky to discover them. Tea and homemade cakes mark your arrival before you are shown around the house and to your lovely, spacious room. There are two guest rooms, one with a super king size bed and the other with twin beds, each with wonderful far-reaching views over the garden, farmland and valley beyond.

Outside, the gardens extend around the house where you will find spring-fed ponds, greatly enjoyed by the many ducks that call Aylworth Manor home, alongside the farm's chickens, sheep and horses.

The Hosts

John and Joanna are the most caring hosts you could wish to stay with. Joanna formerly worked in the City before settling at Aylworth whilst John is a dentist. As well as having a busy family life they also run the farm whilst every other spare minute is spent with their horses which they are passionate about.

The Location

Just a short drive from Bourton-on-the-Water. Close to Stow-on-the-Wold, Sudeley Castle, Chedworth Roman Villa, Snowshill Manor, Hidcote Manor, Kiftsgate Court Gardens, amongst other attractions. Close by is Cheltenham with its music, racing and literature festivals whilst beyond is Gloucester with its historic docks and Cathedral.

The Property

A classic Georgian house in Jane Austen country, The Old Rectory is set in an acre of walled garden in the centre of the village. Glimpses of the church next door can be seen from the large terrace, perfect for eating outside. There is a pond and a croquet lawn in the peaceful garden in which there is colour and interest throughout the seasons. There are some specimen trees which are the owners' pride and joy.

Despite its Georgian appearance, there has been a house on this site from much earlier times. There is a Tudor chimney in the drawing room; Tudor panelling in the sitting room and the cellars are Tudor. The house is traditionally and comfortably furnished and is, above all, a much loved family home.

The Hosts

Friendliness and relaxation are the keynotes in Robin and Phyllida's home. Robin is a retired publisher and Phyllida was, for many years, involved with The Garden Museum (formerly the Museum of Garden History), which was founded by her parents. She organises garden visits in England and abroad and her beautiful garden is testament to the fact that she is an imaginative gardener, whose husband does all the real hard graft!

The Location

It is five miles to Jane Austen's house at Chawton. Portsmouth Dockyard (with HMS Victory, The Mary Rose and Warrior) Gun Wharf Quays and the ferries to the continent and the Isle of Wight are half an hour away. Glorious Goodwood with it racing, classic car events and Festival of Speed is less than 40 minutes drive, as are Winchester and Chichester, with its Cathedral and theatre. Petworth House is close with its Turners and grounds laid out by Capability Brown. There are wonderful walks across National Trust land and the more energetic can walk the Hangers' Way. Heathrow and Gatwick can be reached within the hour.

Robin and Phyllida Smeeton
The Old Rectory,
Headley, Hampshire GU35 8PW
Tel: 01428 714123
phyllida.smeeton@btinternet.com   **1998**

Finding Us

A3 south of Guildford to Hindhead Tunnel. Immediately after tunnel, take first slip road signed Hindhead & Grayshott.
A3 north, take last slip BEFORE the tunnel, signed Hindhead & Grayshott. Go through Grayshott and at Beech Hill garage (approx 4 miles from A3) keep left. Continue to Headley village green, follow road up hill. At top of hill, turn right leaving chestnut tree on island on left and The Hollybush pub on right. House is first drive on left after church.

Rooms (per person per night incl. breakfast)

2 Twin Rooms	£40-£50
(1 en suite / 1 private)	
Single Supplement	£10

Meals

Dinner	£27.50

Opening Times

Closed Christmas, New Year & Easter

Payment Options

Facilities & Services

The Property

How Park Farm, a glorious flint and chalk house dating from the 14th century, overlooks the River Test - offering arguably the finest chalk stream fishing in the world. The Clarendon Way runs by the gate, and for the trout fishermen, the imaginatively restored John of Gaunt lakes are just a five minute walk away.

The house is tastefully decorated, warm, comfortable and a real home. There is a well stocked library for bookworms, a piano waiting to be played in the drawing room and a secluded walled garden and orchard to enjoy with apple, plum and greengage trees.

The large double room features original oak beams, a blue draped canopy bed and an en suite bathroom. It is south facing with views over the valley and The Forest of Bere.

The Host

Caroline has restored a gravel quarry into seven acres of landscaped garden and enjoys walking her guests around the area and explaining how it all came to be, from gravel extraction 70 years ago. The dogs, peafowl, guinea fowl and various ducks lend colour to the scene.

Although Caroline does not now do dinners, in walking distance the Crown pub in the village is friendly and excellent or Stockbridge with The Google Foodie Award is seven minutes by car and has several excellent eating places.

Caroline's breakfasts are a memorable occasion with fresh eggs from the hens, homemade jams and marmalades and always fresh compote of fruit from the garden.

The Location

To the north lies Stockbridge, famous for its coaching inns, fishing, antiques and art galleries. Winchester, the ancient capital of England is south east, with the New Forest and Romsey to the south. Salisbury, with its magnificent Cathedral, and Stonehenge, is to the west. Goodwood for racing and motor racing and Beaulieu with its famous motor museum are also within easy reach. Easy first stop from Dover ferries or Eurotunnel.

Mrs C J Halse
How Park Farm
King's Somborne
Nr Stockbridge
Hampshire SO20 6QG
Tel: 01794 388716
info@howparkfarm.com
www.howparkfarm.com   1997

Finding Us

From Stockbridge take A3057 south towards Romsey, upon entering King's Somborne take the first right up Cow Drove Hill. By seat at top of hill turn left at How Park sign and proceed along the tarmac road for $1/3$ mile to T-junction. Continue then for 100 yards on gravel track, turning right by How Park Farm sign (in paddock) through black gate.

Rooms (per person per night incl. breakfast)

1 Double Room (en suite)   £60

Meals

Breakfast only

Opening Times

Closed occasionally

Payment Options

Facilities & Services

Harry & Sarah Verney
The Garden House,
Cheriton,
Alresford,
Hampshire SO24 0QQ
Tel: 01962 771352 or 01962 771666
sarah@gardenhouseinfo.co.uk   **1984**

Finding Us

From Winchester (A34/M3 Junction 9), after approx 5 miles on A272, turn left at Cheriton / Beauworth crossroads. After 0.7 miles turn left into drive (after the Flower Pots Inn and before the high wall).

Rooms (per person per night incl. breakfast)

1 Double Room (en suite)		**£55**
1 Twin Room (en suite)		**£55**
1 Twin Room, ground floor (private)		**£52**
Single Supplement		**£25**
(2 night bookings preferred)		

Meals

Dinner – by prior arrangement	**£35**

Opening Times

Open all year

Payment Options

Facilities & Services

The Property

Cheriton is an idyllic English village with a Norman church and the Itchen stream running gently through the village green. At The Garden House Harry and Sarah extend the warmest of welcomes to their guests with a delicious tea.

Built in the grounds of the Queen Anne rectory, which was owned by Harry's family, The Garden House is beautifully decorated and furnished. The sweeping staircase is hung with illustrious ancestors and the comfortable, welcoming bedrooms and bathrooms look over the walled garden or surrounding countryside. There is a tennis court which energetic guests are welcome to use.

Sarah, a Cordon Bleu cook, will ensure guests enjoy fabulous food and Harry will entertain with stories of local history including the Battle of Cheriton 1644.

The Hosts

Harry and Sarah are sociable and interesting hosts who enjoy entertaining. Harry is a retired Chartered Accountant who loves sailing and looking after guests. Sarah, as well as her interest in food and cooking, is also passionate about children having the best start in life and delivers parenting courses. She also enjoys playing bridge and tennis.

The Location

Cheriton is within the South Downs National Park and 15 minutes from the cathedral city of Winchester. A perfect place to explore the South Downs Way and Wayfarers Walk, Jane Austen's House, Grange Park Opera and the Georgian market town, Alresford. Alresford has a steam railway, The Watercress Line (Thomas the Tank Engine) and 18-hole golf course. National Trust gardens and houses include Hinton Ampner, Uppark, Mottisfont Abbey and The Vine. Oxford, the New Forest, Chichester theatre, racing at Goodwood, Portsmouth (the historic ships The Mary Rose and Victory), Southampton (the Boat Show, airport, and cruises) are an easy distance, as are Salisbury and Stonehenge. Enjoy excellent local eating, and a real ale pub in the village.

The Property

Winchfield House has been the home of Henrietta's family, the Charringtons, for the last five generations. This magnificent Grade II listed Georgian house, built in 1760, was recently renovated by Henrietta and is filled throughout with family antiques and glorious paintings. The bedrooms and bathrooms are spacious and comfortable with imaginative fabrics used to stunning effect.

The house is surrounded by a large garden, swimming pool, parkland and a lake. The Dressage School operates from the 19th century stable block, and dressage classes can often be watched from the arena in the old walled garden.

The Hosts

Henrietta recently married Andrew Wigram. They are both great fun, vivacious and sociable and thoroughly enjoy welcoming guests to their house. Both are energetic organisers and have travelled extensively around Europe and Australasia. Henrietta is on the Board of an American Charity School in Cambodia and they both go and teach there every year. Andrew, who was formerly in the Army and a farmer, runs a bespoke travel business around Britain. Adrian and Ramona, who come from Romania, assist Henrietta and Andrew with the Wolsey Lodge guests and are first class cooks.

The Location

Superbly located in the heart of the countryside near to the M3, there is easy access to London, Heathrow Airport, Windsor and Ascot. London is under one hour by train from Winchfield Station. Other local places of interest are West Green House (garden open and opera season July/August), The Vyne (National Trust), Stratfield Saye and the charming Georgian village of Odiham. Winchester, Salisbury and Portsmouth are all within an hour by car, as are many race courses.

Henrietta Wigram
Winchfield House
Odiham Road
Hook
Hampshire RG27 8BS
Tel: 01252 843181
henrietta2112@yahoo.com   **1983**

Finding Us

From M3 take Junction 5. Take exit to Farnham (A287) over small roundabout and keep on same road. After 1 mile turn left on B3016 signed Hartley Wintney. Continue for 3 miles (do not turn right for station). Pass under M3, entrance is 200 yards on right through white gateway.

Rooms (per person per night incl. breakfast)

2 Double Rooms	(en suite)	£65
1 Twin Room	(private)	£65

Meals

Supper	£25
Dinner	£35
(Both by prior arrangement)	

Opening Times

Closed Christmas & New Year

Payment Options

Facilities & Services

The Property

Situated on the edge of the pretty black and white village of Dilwyn, The Great House bowls guests over with its beauty, comfort and quiet splendour. Given that Charles II is reputed to have danced on the landing, it is perhaps not surprising that guests are offered a welcome fit for a king! The older part of the house dates to 1550.

The flag-stoned hall with its huge fireplace, beams and panelling opens on to a galleried oak staircase hung with family portraits. The house is furnished throughout with sumptuous fabrics, antiques and paintings. Guests have their own elegant sitting room and the bedrooms overlook the garden, open under the National Gardens Scheme. Visitors are welcome to enjoy the yew walk, rose garden and intricate knot garden.

The Hosts

Tom used to teach at a local prep school and Jane is closely involved with local charity work. Both are deeply committed to the house and garden as well as looking after the two Pekingeses. Locally produced food is used for breakfast and dinner.

The Location

Hay-on-Wye, famous for books and its annual literary Festival is close by and Ludlow has an ancient castle, markets and Michelin starred restaurants. Antique shops, National Trust properties and wonderful gardens abound. Hereford has a great cathedral, ancient chained library and the Mappa Mundi. Several good golf courses within easy reach.

Tom & Jane Hawksley
The Great House, Dilwyn
Herefordshire HR4 8HX
Tel: 01544 318007
greathousedilwyn@googlemail.com
www.greathousedilwyn.co.uk   5968

Finding Us

From Hereford: Take A4110 north for approximately 9 miles. Turn left to Dilwyn. (Ignore sign to Little Dilwyn). At village green bear left. The Great House is on the right with tall wrought iron gates.
From Leominster: Take A44 (signed Brecon) for approximately 5 miles. Turn left into village. Go round three sharp bends. The Great House is on the right hand side.

Rooms (per person per night incl. breakfast)

1 Super King Double Room	(en suite)	**£55**
1 King Size Double Room	(en suite)	**£50**
1 Twin Room	(en suite)	**£55**
Single Supplement		**£10**

Meals

Supper	**£22.50**
Dinner	**£27.50**

(Both by prior arrangement)

Opening Times

Closed Christmas & New Year

Payment Options

£ C

Facilities & Services

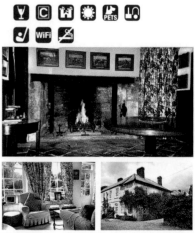

The Property

Dippersmoor Manor is a glorious mix of architectural styles encompassing medieval, Tudor and Georgian features set in its own extensive grounds amid beautiful rolling countryside. Inside, rooms feature fine wood panelling, vaulted and beamed ceilings, inglenook fireplaces, wood burning stoves and flag-stoned floors. Outside there is a wonderful garden to enjoy with a vine and clematis covered pergola where guests can sit amid the scent of roses, lavender and sweet peas and enjoy the blissfully quiet surroundings with views of the Black Mountains in Wales and the rolling Herefordshire countryside.

The bedrooms are beautifully appointed and all have newly refurbished en suite bathrooms offering every comfort. Guests are offered tea and delicious cakes on arrival and a fabulous full English breakfast. By prior arrangement, you may have a three course dinner at Dippersmoor or perhaps chose from one of the many nearby pubs and restaurants.

The Hosts

Amanda and Hexie have devoted 30 years to transforming their house and garden into the haven it is today. Hexie has enjoyed a varied career but now devotes himself to the house, the farm and their guests whilst Amanda, a Cordon Bleu cook, produces exquisite meals and loves gardening. They both have an outstanding knowledge and love of the area and are keen to help their guests enjoy a memorable stay.

The Location

Situated between the beautiful Cathedral city of Hereford (one of the venues for the Three Choirs Festival and home of the Mappa Mundi), the historic market town of Ross on Wye and the lovely Welsh town of Abergavenny, Dippersmoor Manor is just outside Kilpeck and this area of Herefordshire has something for everyone. The annual Hay on Wye Literary Festival is within easy reach as are the Black Mountains and it is a great area for walking, biking, canoeing, golf, fishing and for visiting churches, houses and gardens.

Amanda & Hexie Millais
Dippersmoor Manor
Kilpeck
Herefordshire HR2 9DW
Tel: 01981 570209
info@dippersmoor.com
www.dippersmoor.com   5960

Finding Us

Follow signs to Kilpeck from A465 Hereford-Abergavenny road, 7 miles from Hereford 14 miles from Abergavenny. Drive through village past Kilpeck Inn, fork left at end of village following sign to village hall. 150 metres past village hall turn right over cattle grid and up poplar tree lined drive. Do not use Satnav.

Rooms (per person per night incl. breakfast)

2 King Size Double Rooms (en suite)	£50
1 Emperor double or Twin Room (en suite)	£50
Single Supplement	£20

Meals

Dinner (3 courses by prior arrangement)	£35

Opening Times

Closed occasionally

Payment Options

Facilities & Services

John & Kathy Handby
Caradoc Court
Sellack
Ross-on-Wye
Herefordshire HR9 6LS
Tel: 01989 730257 or 07836 296607
kathy@caradoccourt.co.uk
www.caradoccourt.co.uk   5944

The Property

As one of the oldest Wolsey Lodge houses, Caradoc Court was originally built in 1630, although artefacts found under the ballroom offer evidence that a Roman building may once have stood on the site. A devastating fire in 1986 marked the beginning of an extensive renovation project to restore the Jacobean mansion and today it is a sumptuous, graceful and comfortable retreat open to B&B guests and home to hosts John and Kathy Handby.

The galleried 'Great Hall' leads you into the house and a welcoming tea awaits your arrival before you are invited to explore the comfortable sitting rooms, billiards room, the conservatory with its wrought iron beams, the extensive library and panelled ballroom. Upstairs there are four en suite guest rooms that have been carefully and thoughtfully furnished with everything you would expect of a Wolsey Lodge and all take advantage of the views of the Wye valley, river and of course the beautiful gardens.

Outside there is just as much to explore and enjoy including the rose garden, meandering paths around the pond as well as a walk through the woods and meadows to an idyllic spot by the Wye where the only sound is fish leaping from the water.

The Hosts

John and Kathy arrived at Caradoc Court in 2009 and immediately set to remedying the neglected gardens. John is an enthusiastic historian whilst Kathy's passions for cooking and looking after her guests ensure they'll want to return.

The Location

The Wye Valley is simply beautiful. The river is easily explored and fishing, canoeing, walking and cycling can all be enjoyed. Pretty villages and towns such as Ross and Hay-on-Wye offer shops aplenty whilst the larger cathedral cities of Hereford, home to the Mapa Mundi and chained library, and Gloucester, with its historic docks, are both within easy reach.

Finding Us

From J4 of M50 take A40 for Monmouth; at second roundabout turn right onto A49 for Hereford. After half a mile take right turn for Sellack. Follow lane for about 2 miles until you see Lough Pool Inn on the left. The drive for Caradoc Court is just past this on right between two large stone pillars.

Rooms (per person per night incl. breakfast)

3 Double Rooms (en suite)	**£45-£60**
1 Twin Room (en suite)	**£60**
Single Supplement	**£25**

Meals

Breakfast only

Opening Times

Open March to October

Payment Options

Facilities & Services

Peter & Heather Clark
The Noverings
Brook Lane
Bosbury
Ledbury
Herefordshire HR8 1QD
Tel: 01531 641785
info@thenoverings.co.uk
www.thenoverings.co.uk   5943

The Property

Between the market town of Ledbury and the Malverns, in the heart of Herefordshire, The Noverings is an Edwardian country house with a most distinctive atmosphere and a real pleasure for guests to enjoy. Surrounded by 17 acres of woodland and large formal garden, with many seating areas, The Noverings has been in the same family for nearly 50 years and has been recently refurbished to offer guests luxurious and spacious accommodation where 'all the little things that matter' have been thoughtfully provided.

The three capacious guests rooms with comfortable seating areas, large en suite bathroom or shower room, are furnished with fresh fabrics and linen and enjoy fine views across the countryside and garden. Downstairs, original oak panelling and decorative features are redolent of the elegance of the Edwardian era and lend the house a warm and relaxing ambience. A sunny terrace can be enjoyed in the summer or relax in the billiard room on cooler days.

Whether it is smoked salmon with scrambled eggs, pancakes or traditional breakfast made from abundant local fare to excellent local restaurants to suit all tastes, your stay here is complete on every front.

The Hosts

Heather and Peter Clark were both solicitors before taking over The Noverings from Heather's parents. Together they have worked to restore the house and gardens and welcome their many guests to enjoy the house they so clearly love. Both are accomplished cooks and as keen walkers, their local knowledge will help you to make the most of your stay.

The Location

Malvern's Three Counties Show Ground famous for Spring and Autumn Garden Shows and the host cities of the Three Choirs Festival Worcester, Hereford and Gloucester are within easy reach as are Eastnor Castle, Hampton Court Castle, the Forest of Dean, and for walkers and cyclists the Herefordshire Trail and Cider Route.

Finding Us

Detailed directions available on request or at **www.thenoverings.co.uk**

Rooms (per person per night incl. breakfast)

2 Super King Double/ Twin Rooms (en suite)		£50-£60
1 Twin Room (en suite)		£40-£45
Single Supplement		£10-£20

Meals

2 Course supper - by prior arrangement	£20

Opening Times

Open 1 April – 31 October

Payment Options

Facilities & Services

Geoff & Belinda Walters
Brook House
Brook
Isle of Wight PO30 4EJ
Tel: 01983 740535
bookings@brookhouseiow.co.uk
www.brookhouseiow.co.uk   1971

The Property

Brook House is set in a tranquil corner of West Wight, just a 15 minute stroll from the beach and perfectly situated to explore the many and varied facets of the island.

Surrounded by National Trust land, Brook House sits quietly midst three acres of mature gardens where the sunken rose walk and seating areas will entice you to linger awhile and enjoy the views.

Inside the house, a seamless blend of original architecture and more recent renovations that mark the passage of time from its original Georgian construction have resulted in bright, airy and spacious rooms ornamented with fine furnishings, antiques and décor. Open fires and wood burners ensure that even on cooler days, guests will be completely comfortable.

The guest rooms are well appointed with great care taken to ensure guests' comfort. The room on the ground floor can be either a double or twin with private shower room, whilst on the first floor there are two further guest bedrooms, one with en suite bathroom, and the other with en suite shower room. Island sourced fare is of course the order of the day at breakfast and supper.

The Hosts

Geoff and Belinda have owned Brook House since 1998, gradually moving here completely from London. Belinda was a solicitor and Geoff worked in broadcast technology. Geoff is Australian, now very much an 'Islander' and has a keen interest in cider making and fishing as well as model railways when not tending their wonderful garden, whilst Belinda works part time from home as well as enjoying cooking, gardening and walking.

The Location

This island is steeped in history with stunning scenery and 500 miles of carefully maintained footpaths and a wealth of attractions. From historic sites to music festivals the Isle of Wight has so much to offer. Brook is just a few minutes from the south coast of the Island, with the beaches close by.

Finding Us

From B3401 (Newport to Freshwater road) take B3399 at Chessell. After about a mile, pass Brook Church (on left) and on next bend take main road turning to the right, (signed Brook). Then in a few yards, turn right into the gated private road for the Brook House Private Estate. Brook House is in front of you at the bottom of the hill.

Rooms (per person per night incl. breakfast)

2 Double Rooms (en suite)	from **£50**
1 Double/Twin Room (private)	from **£50**
Single Supplement	**£20**

Meals

Supper (2 courses) (By prior arrangement)	**£25**

Opening Times

Closed Christmas & New Year

Payment Options

Facilities & Services

The Property

Two ancient, Oriental plane trees stand guard at the entrance to the drive and a majestic Holm Oak dominates the lawn at Great Weddington, a Regency Grade II listed country house, sitting in splendour in a beautiful English country garden.

Built around 1835 by a master brewer of ginger beer, the classically proportioned house exudes comfort and warmth. The drawing room is mellow and relaxing and leads onto a beautiful stone terrace overlooking the garden. Terracotta book-cloth covers the walls in the dining room, which creates a richly atmospheric backdrop for dinner.

An elegant staircase leads past a stunning arched window to the galleried first floor where there are two spacious and light double or twin bedrooms, both with their own bathrooms and showers. The Garden Room on the ground floor, also with its own bath and shower, opens onto the herb garden.

The Hosts

Kate and Neil love welcoming guests to their home. Trained at Constance Spry, Kate is one of the resident flower arrangers at Canterbury Cathedral and is also a keen gardener. Neil, after many years in the steel industry, runs his own business - a mail order Audio Book Library. He also plays golf at Sandwich and tries to improve his bridge during the winter!

The Location

Canterbury Cathedral draws visitors from across the globe. Worth exploring, too, are Dover and Walmer castles; the ruins of the Roman Fort at Richborough; wonderful gardens at Goodnestone Park; and John Aspinall's Howletts Wildlife Park. Dover is 20 minutes away, so day trips to France are simple.

Kate & Neil Gunn
Great Weddington,
Ash, Canterbury, Kent CT3 2AR
Tel: 01304 813407
Fax: 01304 812531
greatweddington@hotmail.com
www.greatweddington.co.uk   1594

Finding Us

From Canterbury, take A257 to Sandwich, going through Littlebourne and Wingham. On approach to village of Ash, stay on the A257 and turn left at sign to Weddington.

Rooms (per person per night incl. breakfast)

3 Double/Twin Rooms (en suite)	**£55-£65**
Single Supplement	**£25-£30**
	(excl. w/es Apr/Oct)

Meals

Supper (excl. Sun)	**from £30**
Dinner (excl. Sun)	**from £40**
Occasionally, by arrangement	

Opening Times

Closed Christmas & New Year

Payment Options

Facilities & Services

Mrs Raili Fraser
The Old Rectory,
Hallaton, Market Harborough,
Leicestershire LE16 8TY
Tel: 01858 555350
Fax: 01858 555350
oldrectoryhallaton@hotmail.com   **7998**

Finding Us

Take the A47 from Uppingham and turn left at East Norton and follow signs, or take A6 from Market Harborough, turn right onto B6047. After 3 miles turn right. You will then come to Church Langton and follow signs to Hallaton.

Rooms (per person per night incl. breakfast)

1 Single Room	(en suite)	**£47.50**
1 Double Room	(en suite)	**£50**
1 Twin Room	(private)	**£50**
Single Supplement		**£10**

Meals

Breakfast only

Opening Times

Closed Christmas

Payment Options

Facilities & Services

The Property

A long gravelled drive leads to this Grade II former rectory, standing proudly on a hill next to the church in this lovely Leicestershire village in the heart of the rural countryside. The building has many unique features, and was externally decorated using crests and stone figurines dating back to 1732.

Guests are greeted warmly and are offered welcoming afternoon tea served in the drawing room. An imposing oak staircase leads past guest dining rooms and lounge to a galleried landing and beautifully decorated king size, twin and single bedded guest rooms - all with televisions, hospitality trays and quality toiletries.

The bedrooms overlook the traditional fruit orchard, formal topiary yew trees, landscaped flower beds and a walnut tree known to be grown from walnuts taken from a renowned Motte and Bailey castle mound in Hallaton in the 11th century.

The Hosts

Raili was a nursing sister and is now dedicated to making sure guests enjoy all that the family home has to offer, aided by her daughter, Alexandra, who used to work in finance in London.

The Location

The heart of England offers a wealth of historic houses and stately homes to discover. Rutland Water, Britain's largest man-made lake with bird watching, sailing, windsurfing, cycling and fly fishing is close by, not to mention Uppingham, Rockingham Castle, Kelmarsh Hall and many other houses and lovely gardens to visit are nearby. The traditional "Bottle Kicking" village festival dating back to medieval times, takes place in Hallaton on Easter Monday.

The Property
Luxury in Leicestershire's Charnwood Forest awaits at Horseshoe Cottage Farm, recently converted from old stone farm buildings.

On arrival, guests can enjoy tea and Aga baked scones or homemade cakes, served on the terrace or by the inglenook fireplace in the elegant drawing room. Stone flagged floors and large oak beams in many rooms impart a sense of peacefulness and well-being. Traditional antique furniture graces the interior, especially in the pretty en suite guest bedrooms. Individually decorated with quality fabrics and furnishings, they are a haven of relaxation and the ground floor bedroom is ideal for guests less able to climb stairs.

The cottage garden with herbaceous borders, topiary, azalea and heather beds is home to flourishing kitchen gardens and an orchard where hens lay fresh eggs for breakfast. Fields beyond are laced with footpaths and Bradgate Country Park, with its herds of deer and the ruins of Lady Jane Grey's family home, make a perfect pre-dinner stroll. Overnight stabling is available for visitors with horses who wish to ride through Leicestershire's famous hunting country.

The Hosts
Tim, who used to work in the City and Linda, a radiographer and keen gardener, are both well travelled and offer good food, good company and a warm and friendly welcome. Breakfast is a feast and dinner an occasion - clearly Tim and Linda enjoy good food and entertaining!

The Location
Guests are spoilt for choice with so many attractions within an hour: Stratford-upon-Avon, Warwick and Belvoir Castles, National Space Centre, Rutland Water, Peak District, NEC and Mallory and Donnington race tracks amongst others. Just 10 minutes off the M1, 20 minutes from East Midlands airport and mid-way between London and Scotland - this is an ideal stopover for people touring.

Linda and Tim Jee
Horseshoe Cottage Farm,
Roecliffe Road, Hallgates,
Cropston, Leicestershire LE7 7HQ
Tel: 0116 2350038
lindajee@horseshoecottagefarm.com
www.horseshoecottagefarm.com 7982

Finding Us
From South exit M1 at junction 21A onto the A46, take second exit to Anstey & Beaumont Leys. From North exit M1 at junction 23 onto A512 towards Ashby, at the traffic lights turn left towards Cropston. For more details please see the website above or telephone.

Rooms (per person per night incl. breakfast)
2 Double Rooms (en suite)	£50
1 Twin/Double Room (en suite)	£50
Single Supplement	£15

Meals
Supper	£20
Dinner	£25

Opening Times
Open all year

Payment Options

Facilities & Services

Photograph: Iain Richardson Photography www.iainrichardson.com

Andrew Brownridge & Carole Crooke
Glebe House
26 Church Lane, Muston, Nottingham
Leicestershire NG13 0FD
Tel: 01949 842993 or 07947 742413
glebehouse@glebehousemuston.co.uk
www.glebehousemuston.co.uk   7978

Finding Us

Turn from the A1 onto the A52 near Grantham travel 4 miles towards Nottingham. Close to the sign for Leicestershire border turn left at The Gap Inn (signed to Muston). Glebe House is 300 yards on the left hand side of the road. Hosts will collect guests from Grantham or Bottesford train stations.

Rooms (per person per night incl. breakfast)

1 Four Poster Suite (en suite)		£55-£70
1 Double Room (en suite)		£50-£60
1 Four Poster/Twin (private)		£35-£45
Single Supplement		£10-£20

Meals

Supper	£20
Dinner	£30

(Both occasionally by prior arrangement)

Opening Times

Closed occasionally

Payment Options

£ € C TC

Facilities & Services

BYO C ... ...
... ... WiFi ...

The Property

Glebe House is surrounded by sixteen acres of parkland with views of nearby Belvoir Castle and the pretty church. This gracious listed Georgian home, a former rectory, offers luxury accommodation. Despite the Nottingham address it is firmly located in rural Leicestershire, perfectly placed for guests travelling north or south on the A1 to explore Lincoln, Stamford, Nottingham and unspoilt countryside.

The tree lined driveway leads to a warm welcome from Carole and Andrew with tea and home-made cakes. You will feel instantly 'at home' in the splendidly comfortable Music Room and can unwind and relax in this elegant home. Taking inspiration from the house's Georgian heritage, all the guest rooms are spacious, light and beautifully decorated and furnished in keeping with the period of the house. Fine linen, toiletries, WiFi, and the little touches appreciated by guests, like fresh flowers, are all there for you to enjoy.

Outside, are orchards, a huge vegetable garden, stable yard and paddocks, as well as a formal garden with croquet lawn. Local produce is at the heart of the delicious meals, with fresh homemade bread each morning.

The Hosts

Before retirement Andrew was a Headmaster and Lecturer, but also has been a Civil Servant and Wine Shipper. Carole has a long history in the diplomatic service which saw her travel the world. Together they share a love of choral singing, gardening and of course looking after their guests.

The Location

Glebe House with associations with poets George Crabbe and Lord Byron, is perfectly placed for visiting the Vale of Belvoir, an area of natural beauty on the borders of Leicestershire, Nottinghamshire and Lincolnshire. This unspoilt rural area has wonderful villages, churches and National Trust properties to enjoy and Carole and Andrew have information on even more things to do. For walkers and cyclists there is the Viking Way and Rutland Water.

The Property
Hrempis Farm is an 18th century, Grade II listed farmhouse on the Leicestershire/Nottinghamshire border in the heart of the Quorn Hunt country and, whilst enjoying a degree of solitude set amidst its own grounds, is close to the village centre.

Your arrival is marked with a welcoming tea, served before open fires in the drawing room, in the warm sunlit conservatory or enjoy the summerhouse overlooking the gardens and paddock. An abundance of fine art and local pottery adorn the house along with a plentiful supply of books, whilst a full size snooker table, a grand piano and, in the summer, croquet on the lawns can all be enjoyed.

One guest room on the first floor has a four poster bed, whilst the other, with a twin/double bed is on the second floor, both with views across the gardens. With private sitting rooms and bathrooms, each has been furnished with luxury in mind. If travelling on business, Hrempis Farm provides free WiFi and a desk in each suite.

Breakfast is a feast of local and fairtrade produce and supper here is delicious, whilst excellent local pubs and restaurants are within easy reach including the 2 Michelin star Restaurant Sat Bains.

The Hosts
Before bringing up a family Nicki was a journalist and now has her own PR company as well as being a local school governor, parish councillor, National Trust volunteer at nearby Calke Abbey and area president of Save the Children.

The Location
Hrempis Farm is a 'foodies' heaven with the world famous Stilton cheese and Melton Mowbray pork pies made close by. Robin Hood country and the Peak District National Park are within reach and Burghley Horse Trials, Quorn Hunt Meet, Newark International Antiques Fair, racing at Donnington and Mallory Park, cricket at Trent Bridge, rugby, horseracing, theatre and food fairs can all be enjoyed.

Mrs Nicki Dalton
Hrempis Farm
58 Main Street, Rempstone, Loughborough
Leicestershire LE12 6RH
Tel: 01509 881285 or 07725 429749
bookings@hrempisfarm.co.uk
www.hrempisfarm.co.uk   7977

Finding Us
Exit M1J24. Follow A6 towards Hathern, turn left onto A6006. Follow for 5 miles until to traffic lights, straight into Rempstone village. Follow road around bend, Hrempis Farm is on right, facing the turning signed for Wysall. From Loughborough, take A60 towards Nottingham to traffic lights at Rempstone village. Turn right into village, follow road around the bend and Hrempis Farm is on right.

Rooms (per person per night incl. breakfast)
1 Super King Double/Twin Room (en suite)	**£55**
1 Four Poster Double Room (private)	**£55**
Single Supplement	**£20**

Meals
Supper (3 courses)	**£20**

Opening Times
Closed Christmas

Payment Options

Facilities & Services

The Property

Brills Farm enjoys a commanding hilltop position with spectacular views across the Lincolnshire countryside and is part of a working arable and livestock farm, owned and run by the family. Whilst the décor and furnishings in this restored Georgian house reflect the age of the property, concessions have been made to modern day living with the welcome addition of central heating!

In this much loved family home, the old sits comfortably with the new in beautifully stylish bedrooms. Spectacular views can be enjoyed from the cosy beds and in individually designed, period style bathrooms, guests find ultra modern power showers, gleaming baths and plenty of hot water.

The farmhouse is surrounded by countryside and woods in which you can walk for hours on end, or you may prefer to sit and contemplate by the peaceful lake.

Free wireless internet access

The Hosts

While Charlie is busy with the farm, Sophie manages all the details of home and, as an experienced chef, treats guests to relaxation and fabulous food set in beautiful surroundings. Your hosts can also arrange riding, hunting and clay pigeon shooting; just let them know.

The Location

The heart of Lincoln with its stunning cathedral, imposing castle, exclusive boutiques and delicatessens is a mere 15 minutes drive. Cosmopolitan Nottingham is an easy drive and Newark, steeped in Civil War history and famed for its international antiques fair, is 4 miles away on the River Trent. Once an important part of daily transport, the river can now be enjoyed at a leisurely pace on short boat trips in the summer.

Charlie & Sophie White
Brills Farm,
Brills Hill, Norton Disney, Lincoln,
Lincolnshire LN6 9JN
Tel: 01636 892311 or 07947 136228
admin@brillsfarm-bedandbreakfast.co.uk
www.brillsfarm-bedandbreakfast.co.uk 7985

Finding Us

From the A1, take A46 direction Lincoln. At roundabout follow A46. Take the first exit for Norton Disney. At T-junction turn right and follow for ½ mile. Take first left turn, follow for 1 mile and the drive entrance is on right before going up the hill.

Rooms (per person per night incl. breakfast)

2 Double Rooms (en suite)		**£46**
1 Twin Room (en suite)		**£46**
Single Occupancy		**£55-£60**

Meals

Supper	**£20**
Dinner	**£30**

(Available October-April. Other months by arrangement)

Opening Times

Closed Christmas & New Year

Payment Options

Facilities & Services

The Property

The Grade II listed Barn and stables are tucked away in the conservation village of Folkingham. Brushing away dust and the cobwebs during rebuilding, the owners discovered ancient stonework in the walls, apparently 'recycled' in the 17th century from the Norman castle in the village.

Perfectly restored, but with the advantages of underfloor heating and excellent modern plumbing, apart from a separate sitting room, the rest of the barn is open to the roof with a large dining table at one end, and an open fire surrounded by sofas at the other. Antique oak furniture graces the interior, suffused with light through numerous windows and French doors lead guests out of the kitchen into the sunny courtyard garden.

Simply stylish guest rooms, each with excellent power shower, include a twin or double bedded room, and a further double and single room in the wing of the attached stables. Double/twin room enjoys views over the field of grazing Jacob sheep to the church, which is floodlit after dark.

The Hosts

Simon and Jane have farmed until recently and continue to produce, cook and enjoy wonderful fresh local food, including their own home made sausages. Simon flies an ancient aeroplane and Jane drives her pony in an even more antique trap! They have had enormous fun converting their barn and love sharing it with others.

The Location

The village has many interesting buildings including the 'House of Correction', now owned by the Landmark Trust. Country houses, castles, cathedrals and outstanding village churches abound and the nearby coasts and Wolds are perfect for simply getting away from it all.

Jane and Simon Wright
The Barn,
Spring Lane, Folkingham,
Lincolnshire NG34 0SJ
Tel: 01529 497199 or 07876 363292
Fax: 01529 497199
sjwright@farming.co.uk
www.thebarnspringlane.co.uk   7983

Finding Us

From the A15 in Folkingham, turn into Spring Lane alongside the Village Hall, (just below the old school and the Market Place). The Barn is a little way along on the right.

Rooms (per person per night incl. breakfast)

1 Single Room (private)		£50
1 Twin/Double Room (en suite)		£35
1 Double Room (en suite)		£35
Single Supplement		£15

Meals

Supper	£17.50
Dinner	£25

Opening Times

Closed Christmas & New Year

Payment Options

Facilities & Services

The Property

Guests visiting Lincoln and Lincolnshire can take a step back in time and find themselves entranced by an utterly gracious house set in the Lincolnshire countryside which is home to Pam and David Nickerson, two charming hosts.

This Victorian manor house is reached along a tree-lined drive that opens out to manicured lawns and gardens. Built on the site of a former priory, footprints of long-forgotten buildings and a moat can be seen in the grounds close by. Inside is a haven of comfort with antique furniture warming open fires, oak panelling and a minstrel's gallery providing the perfect backdrop to 'made for relaxing' furnishings.

Each of the two large and spacious bedrooms has an en suite bathroom and fine bed linen guarantees a good night's sleep. Downstairs, alongside a relaxed sitting room, guests can make use of the snooker and billiards room or table tennis room which provides a perfectly relaxing end to any day's exploring. Having run many large shoots, Pam knows the perfect recipe to ensure her guests are well looked after, providing a sumptuous morning repast and, if required, a delicious supper, although make sure your appetite is keen, especially if you want to enjoy dessert too! Alternatively there are excellent local eateries close at hand.

The Hosts

Pam and David inherited the family home in 2004 and retired from their shooting sports business in 2009. With a grown-up family and grandchildren, much of their time is devoted to maintaining the exquisite gardens around the house, golf and quietly perfecting their bridge and now of course, looking after their guests.

The Location

North Ormsby Manor is within five miles of the delightful town of Louth which is the capital of the Lincolnshire Wolds and has just won the BBC Countryfile 'Favourite Market Town in Britain' Award. Also within driving distance of Lincoln where the Cathedral and Castle and the wonderful cobbled streets of uphill Lincoln are well worth a visit.

David & Pam Nickerson
North Ormsby Manor
North Ormsby
Louth
Lincolnshire LN11 0TJ
Tel: 01472 840237
pamela@NorthOrmsbyManor.co.uk
www.NorthOrmsbyManor.co.uk 7976

Finding Us

From South take A16 Louth/Grimsby after 3 miles left in Utterby signed North Ormsby, drive is 1 mile on left, through white gates ½ mile to Manor House. From North take A18 until ½ mile from Ludborough. Turn right signed North Ormsby, pass school on left, ignore road to right signed North Ormsby and after 400 years turn right into drive.

Rooms (per person per night incl. breakfast)

1 Double Room (en suite)		£60
1 Twin Room (en suite)		£50
Single Supplement		£15

Meals

Supper (By prior arrangement)	£20

Opening Times

Open all year

Payment Options

£ C

Facilities & Services

BYO 12 🏠 ☀ 🚶 🏌 ♻ 🚭

The Property
This distinguished house in SE14, sits above a carpet of twinkling London lights overlooking the landscaped Telegraph Hill Park.

The cosy, yet spacious, reception rooms are truly welcoming and have a quiet air of elegance which flows through to beautifully decorated and furnished bedrooms and sparkling bathrooms. The Chinese Peony Room has the plushest of carpets, the biggest of beds, the crispest of linens, Chinese porcelain lamps, lacquered panels and kimonos in the wardrobe. Upstairs, the Tulip Room is decorated with tulip and flower prints. The Richmond Room has twin beds, an adjacent private bathroom, and enjoys a view of the garden.

The exquisite garden was laid out by David's late father, Tim who was a great gardener. It is a perfect lure for garden lovers. There are vibrant camellias, two majestic, fully grown magnolias, a catalpa, holly and bay trees.

Wolsey Lodge guests looking for luxury in South London need look no further - you've arrived!

The Host
David Marten and his family have taken over the B&B from David's late mother, Anne. David and Maedhbhina are warm hosts who like to provide the best hospitality for their guests. In addition to bed and breakfast they also run a photography school. They are passionate about food and travel and like nothing more than to go for a good walk with their dogs.

The Location
113 Pepys Road is lucky to have unrestricted parking to make it easy to come and go as you wish, although the nearest mainline and underground station, New Cross Gate, will get you to London Bridge in just 5 minutes and to Westminster in 20. Greenwich, The Cutty Sark, The National Maritime Museum, Dulwich Picture Gallery, Horniman Museum and Tate Modern are places of interest nearby. The City Airport is only half an hour away by car.

David Marten
113 Pepys Road,
London SE14 5SE
Tel: 020 7639 1060
Fax: 020 7639 8780
davidmarten@pepysroad.com
www.pepysroad.com   4696

Finding Us
From Elephant & Castle roundabout, take A2 (New Kent Road, Old Kent Road, New Cross Road), proceed till turning to Sainsburys Supermarket. Turn left into this turn, then turn right to get back to New Cross Road. After short distance, turn left into Pepys Road, go up the hill, No. 113 is opposite Telegraph Hill Park.

Rooms (per person per night incl. breakfast)

1 Double Room (en suite)		**£55**
1 Double/Twin (en suite)		**£55**
1 Twin Room (private)		**£55**
Single Supplement		**£30**

Meals
Breakfast only

Opening Times
Open all year

Payment Options

Facilities & Services

The Property

Tucked away in the heart of Wimbledon village is an exquisite Edwardian house, home to Ronnie and Sue Dunbar and affable Labrador, Wallace. This large house is split into four apartments and Flat 1A spreads out across the ground floor to a bright conservatory overlooking the gardens. The All England Lawn Tennis Club is on the doorstep, Wimbledon Common is just a short stroll away and you are rarely more than a few minutes from designer shops and cafes aplenty.

Ronnie and Sue are Scottish and together run an interior design business which is evident throughout the house where carefully selected furnishings are interspersed with antiques and modern conveniences like the walk-in shower in the en suite bathroom. The Aga is the central point of the kitchen and meals are enjoyed around the table.

The guest bedroom is well equipped for a comfortable stay and the adjoining sitting room is yours to use exclusively – a great retreat after a day's sightseeing. There is also a small single bedroom available if travelling with a child aged 10 or over. Tea and cake on arrival, delicious breakfasts and dinner if pre-arranged go hand in hand with conversation and laughter to make this Wolsey Lodge a real gem.

The Hosts

Ronnie is a chartered accountant with a keen interest in golf and most other sports and Sue was a nurse before turning her skilled hand to interior design and her other interest is evident in the gorgeous garden here.

The Location

This is such a convenient location - everything is so readily to hand either walking distance, tube or taxi. Shops, tourist attractions and memorable sights can be combined with the enjoyment of London's parks, the closest of which is the 1000 acre Wimbledon Common.

Ronnie & Sue Dunbar
Flat 1A, Alvington House
42 Marryat Road
Wimbledon
London SW19 5BD
Tel: 0208 9468184
sueandronnie2005@yahoo.co.uk　　**4693**

Finding Us

By train from Waterloo to Wimbledon. By tube: District line to Wimbledon. Detailed instructions available on request.

Rooms (per person per night incl. breakfast)

1 Twin Room	(en suite)	**£50**

Meals

Supper	**£20**
Dinner	**£28**

Opening Times

Closed Christmas, New Year & Wimbledon fortnight.

Payment Options

Facilities & Services

Richard and Georgia Bassett
Church Farm House,
Church Road, North Lopham,
Diss, Norfolk IP22 2LP
Tel: 01379 687270 or 07920 488201
Fax: 01379 687270
hosts@bassetts.demon.co.uk
www.churchfarmhouse.org   3994

Finding Us

Take the A11 to Thetford then A1066 towards Diss. At South Lopham turn to North Lopham in front of White Horse Pub. Continue about 1 mile. Church Farm House is opposite North Lopham church.

Rooms (per person per night incl. breakfast)

1 Single Room	(en suite)	**£50**
1 Double Room	(en suite)	**£50**
1 Twin Room	(en suite)	**£50**
Single Supplement		**£10**
(For double/twin rooms)		

Meals

Dinner	**£30**

Opening Times

Closed January

Payment Options

Facilities & Services

The Property

The Bassetts will greet you with a warm Anglo-American welcome, ably assisted by Bonnie the Dog, as you arrive at this beautifully restored Grade II listed thatched Norfolk farmhouse. The interior is light, the inglenook fireplace offers the opportunity for warm fires on cold winter evenings, and the conservatory offers a place to enjoy the gardens and birds in all seasons while eating breakfast, sipping tea or enjoying pre-dinner drinks. It is a well-loved home, a perfect place to share warm hospitality, friendship and good food.

The three en suite bedrooms on the first floor (Rossini, Vivaldi and Verdi) are named for composers as befits the home of two musicians. All have fine views of the old flint St Nicholas Church. Both the Bassetts are avid cooks who especially enjoy dining with their guests by candlelight, and sharing with them inventive food using the best of the local ingredients available. The food and décor of the house are both enhanced by their travel experiences in many lands.

The garden at Church Farm House is just under an acre, with two ponds to enhance its charm. Richard prides himself on the changing seasonal displays that the garden offers. Especially colourful are the many varieties of spring tulips, the brilliant summer begonias, late summer dahlias and the hanging baskets filled with winter pansies. The patio, gazebo, swing and hammock all offer comfortable outdoor seating.

The Hosts

Richard and Georgia Bassett originally came to England to teach music. After their international teaching career, they moved to North Lopham where they enjoy sharing life in the countryside with their guests. Church Farm House is also the headquarters for The Association for Music in International Schools, an international music charity which they founded.

The Location

Church Farm House is well situated for visits to Norwich, Bury St. Edmunds, the Suffolk heritage coast, the North Norfolk coast, the Broads and a host of National Trust houses and gardens.

The Property

Tuttington Hall is a rather special, Grade II listed 18th century house surrounded by beautifully maintained gardens and beyond these the farmland that your host David's family have farmed for some 80 years.

Together David and Andra have managed to create a wonderful haven of peace and tranquillity for their guests. On arrival, home baked scones, cakes and tea are served in the spacious drawing room which is comfortably furnished with old family pieces and where a welcoming fire awaits in the colder months. A candlelit dining room or informal garden room provide the perfect backdrop to the delicious meals provided which feature home produced meat and champion sausages. Eggs, bread, fruit, and vegetables are all either home produced or sourced locally. Fish and shellfish from the coast, with Cromer crabs a local favourite.

The bedrooms, which include a family friendly suite, each have a spacious en suite bathroom and are delightfully decorated and furnished, with fine linen and towels. And each room offers views across the gardens and surrounding countryside.

The Hosts

Andra and David lead very busy lives but despite this they are the most hospitable hosts who go out of their way to ensure that their guests' needs are met. They are both enthusiastic cooks and are justifiably proud of the home produced meat and vegetables they serve.

The Location

Tuttington Hall is within easy reach of both the North Norfolk coast with its wide sandy beaches and the stunning Norfolk Broads. There are both links and inland golf courses only a short drive away. There are a number of historic houses and gardens including Blickling Hall, along with the attractive market towns of Holt and Aylsham. The 'Fine City of Norwich' with its' magnificent Cathedral and Castle combine to make this a fascinating destination.

David & Andra Papworth
Tuttington Hall
Tuttington, Norwich
Norfolk NR11 6TL
Tel: 01263 733417
david@tuttingtonhall.co.uk
www.tuttingtonhall.co.uk   3977

Finding Us

From Norwich head north on A140, on approach to Aylsham, at roundabout take 3rd exit, signed Cromer. Then take 3rd right signed Tuttington; through village, at T-junction turn right, pass church on left, 300m turn right into long gravel drive.

Rooms (per person per night incl. breakfast)

1 Super King Double/Twin Room (en suite)		**£60**
1 King Double	(en suite)	**£50**
1 Single Room	(en suite)	**£50**
Single Supplement		**£15**

Meals

Dinner	**£32.50**

Opening Times

Closed Occasionally

Payment Options

Facilities & Services

William Ellis & Denis Phelan
Seven Acres House
Great Hautbois
Coltishall
Norfolk NR12 7JZ
Tel: 01603 736737
william@hautbois.plus.com
www.norfolkbroadsbandb.com 3967

Finding Us
B1150 towards North Walsham as far as Coltishall. Seven Acres House is located half a mile from Coltishall High Street. Detailed directions will be sent on booking.

Rooms (per person per night incl. breakfast)

1 Double Room	(en suite)	£43-£53
1 Twin Room	(en suite)	£43-£53
Single Occupancy		£65

Meals
Breakfast only

Opening Times
Closed Christmas & New Year

Payment Options

Facilities & Services

The Property
Surrounded by open countryside on the edge of the Broads, Seven Acres House, as the name suggests, is set in extensive grounds with lawns, a woodland dell and meadow. An Edwardian house and home to William and Denis since 2004, it is furnished in an individual style with well-loved family pieces and items reflecting a lifetime's collecting.

A delicious locally-sourced breakfast is served in the bright morning room where guests may relax when they arrive and during their stay. In the warmer months, guests may enjoy afternoon tea among the seasonal array of scented flowers on the terrace overlooking the grounds.

Two comfortable south-facing guest rooms overlooking the garden are furnished in keeping with the style of the house; there are interesting books, a delightful tea tray and en suite bathrooms with many extra thoughtful touches.

The Hosts
William and Denis found Seven Acres (a former fruit farm) tucked away in this quiet yet convenient part of Norfolk shortly before retiring early from their careers in London. Charming and lively conversationalists, they are perfect hosts offering an intimate knowledge of the best places to visit in the area and providing a warm welcome that sees guests returning time and again.

The Location
Boat Trips on the Broads are a feature of any stay here (nearby you can board the steam train which connects with boat trips at Wroxham). Not to be missed are the remarkable East Ruston 30 acre exotic garden, National Trust properties such as Blickling and Felbrigg and fascinating Norwich. Explore Holt with its arts and antiques or the magnificent Holkham Estate which are within easy reach as are fabulous beaches and nature reserves for bird watching. The location is ideal for walking and cycling (local hire available). Restaurants and pubs offer fine dining close by.

Robin & Elisabeth Ellis
Manor House Farm
Wellingham
King's Lynn
Norfolk
PE32 2TH
Tel: 01328 838227
Fax: 01328 838348
libby.ellis@btconnect.com
www.manor-house-farm.co.uk   3962

Finding Us

Wellingham is 7 miles from Fakenham and 9 miles from Swaffham, ½ mile off the A1065 north of Weasenham. Manor House Farm is beside the church in Wellingham.

The Property

In search of peace and quiet? Then consider the perfect retreat at Manor House Farm. Standing alongside the village church the farm has been home to Libby and Robin for over 40 years and in this time they have transformed it into a beautiful country house with a garden that visitors flock to. Tea and homemade cakes or cookies will mark your arrival.

The converted stable wing, with central heating, is across the courtyard and has two large, airy bedrooms with en suites, a spacious sitting room with wood burning stove and a small kitchen. The twin room has wheelchair access. In the main house there is a double bedroom with en suite bathroom. Furnished to ensure guests' absolute comfort, it is easy to understand why guests return to Manor House Farm time and again.

The four acres of gardens include a striking avenue of pleached limes, an abundance of roses, a sunken courtyard garden and an ornamental greenhouse. Breakfast is served in the dining room overlooking the lawn and home-reared pork, garden fruit and eggs from the family hens are offered and cooked to perfection. A good selection of local restaraunts and pubs offer evening meals and Libby and Robin are more than happy to make recommendations. Guests' horses can be stabled here by arrangement.

The Hosts

Robin and Libby have farmed here since 1966, bringing up their four children in what is very much a comfortable family home. Robin is a conservationist and they both have a huge interest in the garden, as well as being widely travelled.

The Location

Once part of the Holkham estate, Manor House Farm is perfectly located to explore the North Norfolk coast, marshes and beaches, Houghton Hall, Sandringham, Blicking, Felbrigg, Oxburgh and Holkham Hall itself as well as Burnham Market, Norwich and Holt and the seal trips from Blakeney are not to be missed.

Rooms   (per person per night incl. breakfast)

2 Double Rooms (en suite)		**£50-£55**
1 Twin Room (en suite)		**£50-£55**
Single Occupancy		**£65-£75**

Meals

Breakfast only

Opening Times

Open all year

Payment Options

Facilities & Services

Liz Jarrett
Colledges House, Oakham Lane,
Staverton, Nr. Daventry,
Northamptonshire NN11 6JQ
Tel: 01327 702737 or 07710 794112
lizjarrett@colledgeshouse.co.uk
www.colledgeshouse.co.uk   4999

Finding Us
Take the A425. From Daventry, turn right
100 yards after Staverton Park Conference
Centre and Golf Course into the village, then
first right, keep left, at give way sign turn sharp
left and Colledges House is immediately on
the right. From Leamington, turn left at The
Countryman pub, keep right, at the Green
keep straight on into Oakham Lane and
Colledges House is the last house on the left.

Rooms (per person per night incl. breakfast)

1 Single Room	(en suite)	**£69.50**
2 Double Rooms	(en suite)	**£47.50-£49.50**
1 Twin Room	(en suite)	**£47.50-£49.50**
Single Supplement		**£20**

Meals
Dinner	**£35**

Opening Times
Open all year

Payment Options

Facilities & Services

The Property
A wonderful welcome awaits in this beautiful Grade II
listed, large thatched Northamptonshire stone cottage, with
converted barn, conservatory and secluded garden.

There's something special at every turn. Winter evenings
are spent in front of a roaring fire in the stunning drawing
room. For summer serenity, enjoy the cottage sitting room
with its Bechstein piano, or wander into the conservatory
to sit and read, away from it all.

Bedrooms in both the main house and cottage are uniquely
and individually decorated - a Jacobean trunk in the single,
Gothic headboards in the twin - a beautiful bureau in the
bathroom. Beds are hugely comfortable and bathrooms
include both bath and shower.

The beautiful garden creates surprises in formal and
informally designed 'rooms', with harmony and colour
contrasts in the inspired planting. Sit on the terrace and
watch koi carp swimming in the pond - or relax, listening
to the waterfall.

The Hosts
Liz is a warm and gregarious hostess and attended the
Cordon Bleu. Her superb meals are legendary with a
dinner party atmosphere, mixing great food, company
and conversation. By prior arrangement, friends or clients
may also be invited.

The Location
The picturesque conservation village of Staverton has
magnificent views over open country. It lies on the Jurassic
Way and The Three River circular walk passes through the
parish. Warwick Castle, Althorp, Woburn and Stratford, are all
within easy reach. Colledges House is within 10 - 20 minutes
of the M1, M6 and M40, so is ideally located for holiday and
weekend breaks, for business or travelling, north or south.

The Property

History and tranquillity are at the heart of Capheaton Hall, a truly special place to stay whilst you explore the many treasures of this beautiful part of Northumberland. Dating back to 1668, it's baroque beauty was later enhanced with Georgian additions, which is how visitors find it today.

The Swinburne family have played an important role in this area of Northumberland since the 12th century. Eliza and Will Browne-Swinburne took over in 2008 and set about renovations to open this fascinating home to guests. The wooded driveway leads you to the impressive Georgian north front courtyard before you enter the East Wing where the family live and welcome guests. The rest of the house is only opened occasionally for tours, so privacy and seclusion are assured.

Tea and delicious cake await your arrival and, as Eliza is a most excellent and inventive cook, will help provide you with a taster for the fine food you will enjoy during your time here. Antiques and comfortable furnishings in the drawing and dining room sit alongside ancestral portraits whilst in contrast there is a stunningly modern kitchen.

There is one en suite double guest room and a double with private bathroom. Outside, the large walled garden, lovingly tended by Eliza provides much of the household vegetables and fruit. Beyond this the parkland and woodland extend down to the nearby lake.

The Hosts

Brought up at Capheaton Hall, Will is a countryman through and through and utterly passionate about his family's part in this historic house. Eliza, also from Northumberland enjoyed a career in radio and television before turning her attention to her family, the house and the gardens.

The Location

Northumberland is a treasure trove of history, beautiful breath-taking coastline and wildlife. Wallington House, Belsay Hall and Alnwick Castle are all close by as is Hadrian's Wall whilst Newcastle city centre boasts excellent shopping, restaurants and theatre.

Will and Eliza Browne-Swinburne
Capheaton Hall
Capheaton
Newcastle on Tyne
Northumberland NE19 2AB
Tel: 01830 530159 or 07900 013269
elizab-s@hotmail.co.uk
www.capheatonhall.co.uk   8952

Finding Us

From South: Newcastle A1 exit A696 Ponteland, Belsay & Jedburgh. 5 miles after Belsay turn left to Capheaton. In village turn left down private road through gates. Turn right down to front of house, park on left side of lawn. From North: A68 into A696 at Otterburn, continue south towards Newcastle, 3 miles after Kirkwhelpington turn right to Capheaton.

Rooms (per person per night incl. breakfast)

1 Double Room (en suite)		£70
1 Double Room (private)		£60
Single Supplement		£20

Meals

Supper	£20
Dinner	£30

Opening Times

Closed Christmas, New Year & Easter

Payment Options

Facilities & Services

The Property

As perfect a Northumbrian country farmhouse as you could wish to find. Welcoming open fires in winter, comfortable furnishings for relaxation and gardens with fine views over stunning countryside. Built in the early 1800's, Preston House is in the hamlet of Preston, close to Alnwick and home to George and Deborah Philipson since 2009. Newly refurbished, Preston House offers all the modern comforts you could wish for and yet still retains many of the fine features of the original house complemented by antiques sitting gracefully alongside more contemporary furniture and décor.

Each guest room has been lavishly furnished with everything a guest could need for a comfortable night's sleep whilst the en suite shower and bathrooms offer luxury toiletries aplenty. Once rested then breakfast here provides a memorable start to the day with a tempting choice of fayre including Craster kippers, scrambled egg and smoked salmon, fresh fruit and a delicious range of preserves. Supper can be arranged for guests and, just like the breakfast, is sumptuous – the venison casserole is particularly delicious!

The gardens offer the chance to try a little croquet or just to sit awhile and enjoy the simple splendour of a corner of Northumberland.

The Hosts

Up until November 2009 George and Deborah and their family had been farming for generations. A change of lifestyle brought them to Preston House and now its restoration is complete Deborah finds the time to paint whilst George enjoys the challenges of refurbishing old Northumbrian properties.

The Location

Preston House is perfectly located mid-point between Newcastle-upon-Tyne and Edinburgh. Northumberland offers something for everyone – sandy beaches, miles of Hadrian's wall to explore, Bamburgh, Alnwick, Warkworth and Dunstanburgh castles. Farne, Coquet and Holy Islands, Cragside, Wallington and Paxton Houses and gardens.

George & Deborah Philipson
Preston House
Chathill, Alnwick
Northumberland NE67 5DH
Tel: 01665 589461 or 07817 175609
Fax: 01665 589461
info@northumbrian-escapes.co.uk   **8948**
www.northumbrian-escapes.co.uk

Finding Us

Off A1 signed Ellingham, Doxford and Preston and brown tourist sign for Preston Tower (which is opposite the house). Stay on this minor road, pass signs for Ellingham on left, pass school on left and pass Joiners Bunkhouse on left. Preston House is next on left with stone pillared gateway, swing wide to pass through gate, park at front door.

Rooms (per person per night incl. breakfast)

4 Double/Twin Rooms (en suite)	£42.50-£60
Single Supplement	£25

Meals

Supper (Occasionally by prior arrangement)	£30

Opening Times

Closed Christmas & New Year

Payment Options

Facilities & Services

The Property

Rectory Farm, a beautifully secluded, two hundred and seventy year old, creeper clad Cotswold country house revealed at the end of a tree lined avenue, is situated in its own 450 acre valley of scenic farmland.

Off the traditional flagstoned hall, there is a welcoming drawing room with deep plush sofas and tables laden with interesting books and magazines. In winter, roaring log fires fill the room with life while guests partake of afternoon tea. The elegant dining room features a 14 foot solid oak table.

Three impeccably furnished, comfortable, light and airy bedrooms have lovely views over the three acre garden which leads to two beautiful trout lakes (four and five acres) and woodland. Fishing is available to guests.

The Hosts

Nigel, an arable and livestock farmer, and Elizabeth both enjoy all aspects of country living. Having lived here all their lives, they possess good local knowledge and are only too happy to advise on the more unusual places to visit.

The Location

Halfway between Stratford-upon-Avon and Oxford, 22 miles from Cheltenham, 5 from Stow-on-the-Wold and 11 from Blenheim Palace, makes Rectory Farm an ideal centre for touring the Cotswolds. Warwick Castle, Chastleton and Rousham Houses, Hidcote and Bourton House Gardens are within easy reach. There is something for everybody, including a popular walk from the house to the Rollright Stones (a Bronze Age stone circle).

Nigel & Elizabeth Colston
Rectory Farm,
Salford, Chipping Norton,
Oxfordshire, OX7 5YY
Tel: 01608 643209 or 07866 834208
enquiries@rectoryfarm.info
www.rectoryfarm.info   5991

Finding Us

Salford is one mile north-west of Chipping Norton off the A44. Rectory Farm is at the far end of the village. Go past the Black Horse pub, left at the telephone box (Cooks Lane), up the hill, past the children's play area on your right and then left into the farm drive. Continue for 200 yards through the avenue of trees, and turn left into the house and gardens.

Rooms (per person per night incl. breakfast)

2 Double Rooms	£46-£50
(1 en suite/1 private)	
1 Twin/Double Room	£46-£50
(en suite)	
Single Supplement	£15-£25

Meals

Breakfast only

Opening Times

Closed 1st December - 1st February

Payment Options

Facilities & Services

The Property

Home Farmhouse, Charlton is nearly 500 years old and retains many of its original features – beams, inglenook fireplaces and winding staircases. Most important of all, though, is the feeling of friendliness and warmth which many guests remark on when they enter the house for the first time. The house itself could not be more conveniently laid out for guests with three charming bedrooms each enjoying its own approach staircase and en suite bathroom. The bedrooms have extremely comfortable beds made up traditionally with sheets, blankets and eiderdown and are provided with television and radio, fresh fruit, chocolates and flapjacks.

Tea and cake are offered to guests on arrival – in the delightful walled garden if the weather permits or in the attractive drawing room if it does not or if the garden is closed under the NGS scheme. Breakfast, to order the night before, including homemade bread, jams and blackberry and apple compote from the garden, is served in the elegant dining room and is usually a lively talkative affair with Nigel's military ancestors looking down approvingly from the walls.

The Hosts

Nigel, Rosemary and Goliath and Samson, two miniature wire haired dachshunds, offer the friendliest welcome. Nigel retired to become Chief Executive of the British Horse Society, prior to which, he spent 32 years in the Army. Rosemary trained as an interior designer and for thirty years has very successfully run her own interior design, soft furnishing and upholstery business.

The Location

From this tranquil setting, you are perfectly placed to enjoy Oxford, Stratford-upon-Avon, Warwick Castle, Blenheim Palace, Waddesdon Manor and Hidcote. Beautiful Cotswold villages such as Chipping Campden, Broadway, Snowshill and the Slaughters are just a stone's throw away and Silverstone Grand Prix, Blenheim Horse Trials and Stowe Opera all take place close by. There is a good friendly pub just 100 yards away – reservation recommended.

Rosemary Grove-White
Home Farmhouse, Charlton,
Nr Banbury, Oxfordshire OX17 3DR
Tel: 01295 811683 or 07795 207000
Fax: 01295 811683
grovewhite@lineone.net
www.homefarmhouse.co.uk   4998

Finding Us

South: leave the M40 at junction 10; follow the A43 towards Northampton. After 5 miles turn left to Charlton. On entering the village turn left down the village street; 100 yards after the pub, turn left into a gravelled lane. From north, leave M40 at Banbury, junction 11; turn left onto A422. After 4½ miles at Farthinghoe turn right to Charlton. Straight down the village street and turn left into gravelled lane 100 yards after the pub.

Rooms (per person per night incl. breakfast)

1 Double Room (en suite)	£44
2 Double/Twin Rooms (en suite)	£44
Single Supplement	£14

Meals

Supper	£22
Dinner	£28

(Both by prior arrangement; min 4 persons)

Opening Times

Closed Christmas

Payment Options

Facilities & Services

The Property
Surrounded by views of undulating countryside and on the edge of a small Oxfordshire village, sits Holmby House. An impressive drive leads to a wisteria clad, elegant Victorian house. On arrival, guests are welcomed with tea and homemade cakes in front of a log fire in the winter or on the terrace in the summer. Inside, the recently restored house is luxuriously decorated with classic fabrics and antique furniture. Bedrooms are spacious and light with fantastic views. Guests are greeted in their rooms by an array of facilities including large comfortable beds, good sized baths or power showers, television, telephone, fresh flowers, a bowl of fruit and bottled mineral water.

The garden is a colourful, fragrant oasis and includes a secluded summer house. For the more active guest, there is an outdoor heated pool, tennis court and croquet lawn.

The Hosts
Sociable and enthusiastic hosts, Sally and John enjoy sharing their home and entertaining. Sally, an ex-Barts ward sister and past England lacrosse player, enjoys all aspects of country living. An aficionado of Claire Macdonald, guests are assured of good cooking from local produce and home grown vegetables. John is a hormone specialist and has a particular interest in wine. Your hosts are keen on opera, theatre and travel - especially to Scotland.

The Location
On the edge of the Cotswolds, there is something for everyone near Holmby House. Stratford-upon-Avon, Stow on the Wold, Chipping Campden, Oxford and Warwick are all within a short distance of the property. There are excellent walking and cycling opportunities not far from the doorstep with golf and horse riding available locally. The village has a number of good pubs and a new, highly rated restaurant.

John & Sally Wass
Holmby House
Sibford Ferris, Nr Banbury
Oxfordshire OX15 5RG
Tel: 01295 780104 or 07968 158598
Fax: 01295 780104
sally.wass@btinternet.com
www.holmbyhouse.com   **4994**

Finding Us
Exit M40, J11, go towards Banbury. At 3rd roundabout (Tesco ahead) left onto Southam Rd. At Banbury Cross roundabout, right onto B4035. After Swalcliffe, at top of hill, left to Sibford Ferris. Straight over, into village. Holmby House is first house on right.

Rooms   (per person per night incl. breakfast)

2 Double/Twin Rooms (en suite)	**£45-£55**
2 Double Rooms (en suite)	**£40-£50**
1 Double Room (private)	**£45-£55**
Single Supplement	**£10**

Meals

Dinner	**£35**

Opening Times
Open all year

Payment Options

Facilities & Services

James & Alison Kerr Muir
Hawkhill House
Nether Worton
Chipping Norton
Oxfordshire
OX7 7AP
Tel: 01608 683355 or 07710 353224
hawkhillhouse@gmail.com
www.hawkhill-house.co.uk   4987

Finding Us

From Oxford / Banbury head for
Deddington. Leave Deddington on B4031
towards Chipping Norton. Go through
Hempton and down steep hill. Take left to
Nether Worton. Hawkhill House is the only
property in the village on the right hand side.

Rooms (per person per night incl. breakfast)

2 Double Rooms (en suite)		**£47.50**
1 Twin Room (en suite)		**£47.50**
Single Supplement		**£15-£20**

Meals

Supper	**£20**
Dinner	**£25**

Opening Times

Closed occasionally

Payment Options

Facilities & Services

The Property

Set amidst the tiny Cotswolds hamlet of Nether Worton,
Hawkhill House is a stone built farmhouse overlooking
immaculate gardens, a pond and paddock, in fact a
perfectly idyllic location. Whilst you enjoy tea and cake
in the drawing room overlooking the garden you will get
to know your hosts. The house is traditionally furnished
with antiques and family photos and heirlooms and
warming open fires in the winter make this a perfect base
throughout the year. In the main house there is a twin
and double room which are both light and spacious and
very comfortably furnished with wonderful views over the
surrounding countryside. Additionally there is a ground
floor annex in a cottage in the grounds which, whilst
separated from the main house, offers easy access and all of
the Wolsey Lodge hospitality you would expect.

Breakfast, and dinner too if you choose to eat in, are served
in the formal dining room, relaxed kitchen or alfresco when
the weather permits and is never less than a culinary treat
with homemade produce, much of it either from the garden
or locally sourced.

Outside, the setting is truly lovely with landscaped gardens
surrounded by paddocks where horses graze. Hawkhill
House can provide stabling for guests' horses and can
organise hunting with any of the local hunts.

The Hosts

The family enjoy welcoming guests to stay. Alison, formerly
the owner of a large catering business, so all things culinary
are close to her heart and the family's dogs and horses are
favourites here too.

The Location

Chipping Norton is perfect for exploring the Cotswolds.
There are extensive walking and cycling routes and many
National Trust properties within a short distance plus Hook
Norton brewery, Daylesford Farm, Upton House, Stowe,
Blenheim Palace, Broughton Castle, Rollright Stones, Stow
on the Wold, Oxford and Rousham.

Hayden & Yvonne Lloyd
Upper Buckton,
Leintwardine, Craven Arms,
Shropshire SY7 0JU
Tel: 01547 540634
Fax: 01547 540634
ghlloydco@btconnect.com
www.upperbuckton.co.uk   5984

The Property

Splendidly set in 400 acres of the unspoilt Teme Valley, this elegant Georgian farmhouse looking south over the river towards the Wigmore Rolls, offers sophisticated hospitality in beautiful relaxed surroundings. A large, mature garden, a masterpiece in light and shade, is brimming with unusual herbaceous plants, flourishing lilies and hostas around a 12th century motte, ha-ha and millstream.

Guests are cosseted in this genteel three storey gentleman's residence, with well proportioned and attractively decorated rooms, containing beautiful antiques and paintings, collected over many years. Elegant bedrooms, with the emphasis on comfortable furnishings, have beautiful cotton appliqué sheets and pillowcases on the lovely beds and en suite or private bathrooms, complete with special finishing touches.

The Hosts

Hayden and Yvonne have been farming at Upper Buckton for over three decades. They have a wide knowledge and love of the surrounding countryside and enjoy introducing their guests to this unspoilt part of the Welsh Borders. They are warm hosts who endeavour to make guests feel immediately relaxed and at home in their haven of peace, good humour and great food. Yvonne's cooking is an imaginative and sophisticated blend of traditional and Cordon Bleu cooking. Hayden takes great care over the wine list, which features the best European and New World wines.

The Location

Visitors will find many interesting places to visit including Ludlow, Much Wenlock, the Black and White Villages of Herefordshire, the Castles: Ludlow, Powis, Croft and Stokesey and National Trust properties and gardens galore. There are many walks in the area and horse riding can be arranged locally.

Finding Us

From Ludlow take A49 north towards Shrewsbury. At Bromfield turn left, A4113 to Knighton. Pass through Leintwardine continuing on A4113 to Walford. Turn right into narrow road signed Buckton. Upper Buckton is in the hamlet of Buckton, third house on the left. Please drive into courtyard.

Rooms   (per person per night incl. breakfast)

1 Double Room	(en suite)	£48-£55
1 Twin/Double	(en suite)	£48-£55
1 Twin/Double	(private)	£48-£55
Single Supplement		£15

Meals

Dinner   £30

Opening Times

Closed Occasionally

Payment Options

Facilities & Services

The Property
Set behind white wrought iron gates in a farming hamlet, Woolston House is the pretty Georgian home of Caroline Evans de Porras who, together with husband Alberto has refurbished the house to offer every modern comfort whilst carefully retaining its original features. The guest rooms are spacious with large, comfortable beds, seating, LCD television, Hi-Fi and refreshment tray with homemade cake or biscuits. The Aston Room, a large double with en suite dressing and luxury shower rooms will be available from 2013. The Sandford Room has an en suite whilst the Maesbury Room has a privately accessed bathroom below. Locally sourced luxury toiletries and bathrobes are provided.

Downstairs the drawing room and dining room have French doors into the garden and in the winter open fires warm guests returning from a days exploring. A delicious breakfast menu features more local fare and dinner, if taken, is accompanied by a fine wine list.

Enjoy a day out meandering along the lanes of Shropshire or exploring the majesty of Snowdonia in one of the beautiful classic cars available for hire.

The Hosts
Caroline and Alberto are settled in Caroline's native Shropshire and have devoted themselves to creating a home that guests can enjoy. Alberto is Spanish and has an IT background as well as a love of the classic cars they offer to guests. Caroline's background is in food safety and technical management in the food industry.

The Location
The Shropshire countryside is a green and pleasant land and Woolston House is perfectly situated for visiting Shrewsbury, Chester, Llangollen, Ellesmere, Oswestry, Lake Vyrnwy, Snowdonia, the Welsh coast, Offa's Dyke, Llanrhaeadr Waterfall (240ft - the highest in the country), Ironbridge Gorge, the Acton Scott Estate the setting for BBCs 'Victorian Farm', National Trust properties, castles and museums.

Mrs Caroline Evans de Porras & Mr Alberto Porras
Woolston House
Woolston, Oswestry
Shropshire SY10 8HY
Tel: 01691 682075
enquiries@woolstonhouse.com
www.woolstonhouse.com   5942

Finding Us
From M54 - A5 bypassing Shrewsbury towards Oswestry. Over 7 roundabouts, at 8th take B4396 through Knockin. After Knockin take first right, signed Maesbury/Oswestry. After 1 mile, take right turn as road bends sharp left. Follow road downhill and as it bends right, Woolston House is in front as road forks. Take right fork, stop in front of white gates or pull into drive.

Rooms (per person per night incl. breakfast)

1 Double/Twin Room	(en suite)	£50-£55
1 Double/Twin Room	(private)	£50-£55
1 Double Room	(en suite)	£50-£55
Single Occupancy		£75-£80

Meals

Supper	£15
Dinner	£25-£35

(Both by prior arrangement)

Opening Times
Closed occasionally

Payment Options

Facilities & Services

The Property

In an elegant residential area of the beautiful market town of Shrewsbury, this substantial Victorian family house has been lovingly restored and many original features, like the stunning tiles in the entrance hall, uncovered. With off-street parking, Hambrook House is a short stroll from the town centre and ideal for visiting the historic county town of Shropshire. It is also popular with visitors to nearby Shrewsbury School.

Reception rooms are extremely comfortable, with lovely antique furniture and paintings to enjoy. A guest sitting room with views of the garden has a piano for anyone wishing to 'tickle the ivories'! Bedrooms are furnished to a very high standard, with pocket sprung mattresses, quality white bed linen, towels and toiletries. All have en suite bath or shower, tea and coffee making facilities, flat screen television and free WiFi. For the less mobile guest there are two ground floor rooms, one with walk-in shower.

Breakfast is served at individual tables in the bright and airy dining room, and produce is locally sourced, with free-range eggs, sausages and bacon.

The Hosts

Charlotte and Kevin moved to Shrewsbury with their young family a couple of years ago, and since opening have rapidly developed an excellent reputation. Kevin is a chartered surveyor and Charlotte had a career in publishing. They are always happy to advise visitors on restaurants, hostelries and other places to visit just a short stroll away.

The Location

With over 600 listed buildings, Shrewsbury is a historic and vibrant market town with a splendid medieval heritage. A veritable 'shopper's paradise' it boasts many independent businesses. It is the perfect base to explore the museums and historic sites of Ironbridge Gorge and the awe-inspiring aqueducts of Pontcysyllte and Chirk.

Charlotte & Kevin Dowd
Hambrook House
13 Kennedy Road, Shrewsbury
Shropshire SY3 7AD
Tel: 01743 365456
charlotte@hambrookhouse.co.uk
www.hambrookhouse.co.uk   5939

Finding Us
Detailed directions available at time of booking.

Rooms (per person per night incl. breakfast)

4 King Size Double Rooms		£47.50-£57.50
1 Double Room	(en suite)	£45
1 Twin Room	(en suite)	£52.50
Single Occupancy		£75- £100

Meals
Breakfast Only

Opening Times
Closed Christmas

Payment Options

Facilities & Services

Martin & Frances Hardman
Pitfour House,
High Street, Timsbury,
Bath, Somerset BA2 0HT
Tel: 01761 479554
pitfourhouse@btinternet.com
www.pitfourhouse.co.uk   5976

Finding Us

Take A367 from Bath to Radstock and
Wells. After 3 miles turn right onto B3115
(Timsbury and Tunley). Continue for 4
miles to Timsbury. Turn left after shops into
Newmans Lane, bearing right into the High
Street. Pitfour House is 50 yards on the right.

Rooms (per person per night incl. breakfast)

2 Twin/Double Rooms	**£44-£49**
(1 en suite/1 private)	
Single Supplement	**£20**

Meals

Dinner	**£27-£32**

Opening Times

Closed Occasionally

Payment Options

Facilities & Services

The Property

Splendid food, convivial company and truly wonderful
hospitality are to be found at Pitfour House, a quintessentially
English experience in a charming Georgian home, which
boasts a beautiful staircase and cupola. Situated in the rural
village of Timsbury just outside Bath, the house, which
stands back from the High Street, has a wonderfully mellow
stone façade, glimpsed beyond large gates.

Tea and home made delicacies are served on arrival, after
which guests may enjoy the comforts of an elegantly
furnished formal sitting room with open fire. There is
another separate, and more relaxed sitting room with
television, and a delightful panelled dining room where
guests dine superbly in the company of their hosts. Being of
typical 18th century proportions, the house also offers well
appointed, comfortable bedrooms with king size Vi-Spring
beds, one with an en suite shower room and the other with
its own adjacent bathroom.

The main ½ acre walled garden is to the rear of the property
and is stocked with mature shrubs and trees, a productive
greenhouse and a thriving vegetable garden.

The Hosts

Martin is a retired paediatrician and enjoys gardening and
furniture restoration. Frances is a retired dentist and is a
keen flower arranger. They both enjoy entertaining and the
challenge of providing good quality food using home grown
produce whenever possible.

The Location

Timsbury is an interesting rural village with many scenic
walks nearby. Bath is within an easy drive, with the great
advantage of a Park & Ride just 4 miles from the house.
Other places of interest include the cathedral city of Wells,
Glastonbury, Tyntesfield and SS Great Britain in Bristol.

The Property

A precious gem in a perfect setting, it is as if time has stood still at Beryl, a beautiful small Gothic mansion standing serenely in 13 acres of parkland, one mile north east of magnificent Wells Cathedral.

Designed and built in 1838, by Benjamin Ferrey, a pupil of Pugin, Beryl has been lovingly restored with Gothic inspired features and a wealth of fine antiques. The elegant drawing room is the perfect place to unwind in luxurious style; the relaxed sitting room is perfect for watching television, playing board games and enjoying a much needed drink. Wells offers excellent dining opportunities from relaxed pubs to upmarket restaurants.

Individually decorated, well appointed bedrooms enjoy views of the cathedral and gardens where an outdoor pool, croquet lawn, restored walled garden and woodland and a children's play area are waiting to tempt guests outside in all seasons.

The Hosts

Holly and her daughter Mary-Ellen continue a tradition of gracious hospitality, started with her late husband in 1980. They share an eye for fine detail, and a complete understanding of how guests love to be treated is evident in this warm and welcoming home.

Guests can enjoy a lovely jewellery boutique run by Mary-Ellen and her husband Edward Byworth in the Coach House.

The Location

At the foot of the Mendips, Beryl is perfect for West Country touring. Wells, the smallest city in Europe and home to its oldest inhabited street is only a mile away. Wookey Hole, Cheddar Caves, Longleat Country House, Stourhead and Montacute House are all within easy reach, with Weston-Super-Mare, Bath and Bristol a little further afield.

Holly Nowell & Mary-Ellen Nowell
Beryl,
Top of Hawkers Lane, Wells,
Somerset BA5 3JP
Tel: 01749 678738
Fax: 01749 670508
stay@beryl-wells.co.uk
www.beryl-wells.co.uk   5995

Finding Us

Leave or approach Wells on Radstock Road B3139. Follow signs to the Horringtons, opposite BP garage turn left into Hawkers Lane (not Beryl Lane) next to bus stop. Drive to top of lane - see sign 'Beryl' - continue up leafy drive, approximately 300 yards to main gate.

Rooms   (per person per night incl. breakfast)

4 Double Rooms (en suite)	**£50-£75**
3 Twin Rooms (en suite)	**£50-£75**
Single Supplement	**£25**
Chair lift to first floor	

Meals

Kitchen Supper (3 courses)	**£30**
(By prior arrangement)	

Opening Times

Closed Christmas

Payment Options

£ C TC VAT ◎ VISA ◎ ▦

Facilities & Services

Michael & Lavinia Dewar
Rectory Farm House
Charlton Musgrove, Wincanton
Somerset BA9 8ET
Tel: 01963 34599
l.dewar@btconnect.com
www.rectoryfarmhouse.com   5971

Finding Us

From East: Exit A303 at B3081 for Blandford Forum & Shaftesbury. Go under A303, left at T-junction, right after Hunters Lodge Pub, signed Charlton Musgrove. Go 1 mile and left into Rectory Lane. After 0.4 miles Rectory Farm House is on right. Follow drive to the yard to park.

Rooms (per person per night incl. breakfast)

1 Double Room	(en suite)	£50
1 Double/Twin Room	(private)	£50
Single Supplement		£20

Meals

Dinner	£35

Opening Times

Closed Christmas & New Year

Payment Options

Facilities & Services

The Property

In its quiet and peaceful location, Rectory Farm House is surrounded by fields and woodland. Binoculars are provided to enable guests to appreciate the wealth of different animals that live in the surrounding area. Deer, owls and buzzards can all be seen on a frequent basis.

The large and imposing Somerset farmhouse has been lovingly restored by Michael and Lavinia and is decorated in traditional English country style with antique furniture and porcelain setting off the architectural attributes.

Once a field, the Dewars have created their six acre formal garden from scratch. Using trees from the landscape, lawn areas with traditional yew hedging intermingle with orchards and a small wood has been planted in the distance.

Tea and homemade cake on arrival. Large double bedrooms, with supremely comfortable beds, offer magnificent views of the surrounding countryside. Tea and coffee making facilities, televisions, fluffy bathrobes, an abundance of books and daily newspapers ensure a delightful stay.

The Hosts

The Dewars are well travelled; Michael is a military historian and has had fourteen books published; Lavinia, a Cordon Bleu cook, meanwhile spends her time developing her large garden. With four children having now left home, family photos and mementoes ensure the house remains a relaxed and welcoming family home.

The Location

The property is set in an Area of Outstanding Natural Beauty and is close to Bath, Salisbury and Wells. It is surrounded by a wealth of classic English gardens and great houses such as Stourhead, Montacute, Longleat, Lytes Carey and Barrington Court. Wincanton Racecourse is close by. Glastonbury Tor, Cheddar Gorge, the Mendips and the Somerset Levels are a short distance away. Excellent local eating.

The Property

Edington House is one of the most spectacular houses you are likely to stay in. Dating from the mid 1600's, character and history abound. Inge and Robert are only the second owners since the house was built, and they have created a wonderful home filled with stunning antiques, beautiful paintings and porcelain. Sumptuous fabrics and vases of flowers from the gardens adorn the rooms and the kitchen garden has plenty of fruit and vegetables.

The beautiful drawing room overlooks the lawn and terrace and many of the other rooms retain original panelling along with fascinating alcoves, arches and fine wooden and stone floors. Bedrooms are spacious, comfortable and beautifully finished (the main bedroom has a four poster bed) and the en suite bathrooms have everything guests could wish for. Inge is an accomplished cook who prepares delicious breakfasts and dinner or supper using local ingredients from local producers and her own freshly made fruit juices.

The gardens are filled with trees, shrubs and flowers and a three acre orchard is home to the family ponies. A Georgian summer house and an arched Georgian alcove provide relaxed seating whilst the more active may use the tennis court and swimming pool.

The Hosts

Inge, Austrian by birth, is a designer by profession and her beautiful home is testament to her talent. Robert is a lawyer and they both share a keen interest in history and architecture.

The Location

Edington House is situated in the historic Somerset Levels. It lies on the north side of the Polden Hills along which runs an old Roman road and nearby are the renowned Glastonbury Tor and Abbey and the site of the Battle of Sedgemoor. Wells, Bath and Stonehenge are all within easy reach along with Cheddar Gorge, Wookey Hole, Dunster Castle, Stourhead and Hestercombe Gardens.

Robert & Inge Sprawson
Edington House
Broadmead Lane
Edington, Bridgwater
Somerset TA7 9JS
Tel: 01278 722238
Fax: 01278 722238
inge@edingtonhouse.co.uk
www.edingtonhouse.co.uk   2966

Finding Us

Leave M5 at junction 23 on to A39 signed to Glastonbury & Wells. After 4 miles take left turn to Edington. After ½ mile on coming in to the village turn left at crossroads. After 200 yards turn right down Broadmead Lane. The house is 100 yards down lane on left behind a wall.

Rooms (per person per night incl. breakfast)

2 Double Rooms (en suite)	**£68**
1 Double Room (private)	**£68**
Single Supplement	**£20**

Meals

Supper	**£25**
Dinner	**£38**

Opening Times

Closed Christmas

Payment Options

Facilities & Services

The Property

Guests who have previously stayed with Maggie and Chris Knight at Cumledge Mill House in Berwickshire will surely be delighted to visit them once again, this time at their home in the delightful setting of Castle Cary. New and old guests alike will quickly realise that the utter peace and tranquillity of The Old Vicarage, although in the centre of town, is just one of the things that make this home so special.

Elegantly furnished, the large dining and sitting room and the stunning two storey conservatory, where guests can relax, provide pleasurable views over the two acres of garden with its sweeping lawns, graceful trees and old stone walls and courtyard. The swimming pool and surrounding terrace with its vine covered pergola are another treat for guests to enjoy – what a joy at the end of a day's sightseeing.

Each guest room has been carefully decorated and furnished with gorgeous fabrics, paintings and interesting artefacts. Taking breakfast from the extensive menu – choose from full English, Scottish or a taste of America – will leave you perfectly set for the day; and dinner, should you choose to eat in, will be a similar gastronomic delight as Maggie is an outstanding cook.

The Hosts

Maggie and Chris are easy-going company and make their guests immediately welcome. Together they have lived in America, India and Bermuda before settling back in the UK and more recently moving to Castle Cary to be closer to their family. Chris was formerly a lawyer and is now a magistrate and Maggie was a nurse.

The Location

Castle Cary is perfectly situated to explore Somerset. Wincanton Racecourse, Glastonbury Tor and Abbey, Wells with its stunning Cathedral, Longleat, Haynes Motor Museum and the fascinating Fleet Air Arm Museum as well as many National Trust properties. The beautiful Mendips and Somerset levels are within easy reach.

Chris & Maggie Knight
The Old Vicarage
Church Street
Castle Cary
Somerset BA7 7EJ
Tel: 01963 350226
mcknightcm@btopenworld.com   **5949**

Finding Us

In Castle Cary continue through the town towards Yeovil (B3152). On your right pass the garage and at All Saints Church turn right into drive which is on the far side of and adjacent to the churchyard.

Rooms (per person per night incl. breakfast)

2 Double Rooms (en suite)	£60
Single Supplement	£15

Meals

Dinner	£30

Opening Times

Closed Christmas & New Year

Payment Options

Facilities & Services

Frances and Tim Meeres Young
Stoberry House
Stoberry Park
Wells
Somerset BA5 3LD
Tel: 01749 672906
stay@stoberry-park.co.uk
www.stoberry-park.co.uk   5955

Finding Us

From Bristol or Bath enter Wells on A39; immediately after 30mph sign turn left into College Road, then left through wrought iron gateway into Stoberry Park. At top of park bear right and follow tar driveway into walled garden.

Rooms (per person per night incl. breakfast)

2 Double Rooms (en suite)	**£40-£67.50**	
1 Twin Room (en suite)	**£45-£55**	
Cooked breakfast on request with small supplement		
Single Supplement	**£35**	
Reduced rates for 2 or 3 night stays.		

Meals

Supper (2 courses)	**£20**
Dinner (3 courses)	**£25**

(Both by prior arrangement and for a minimum of 6 persons)

Opening Times

Closed Christmas

Payment Options

Facilities & Services

The Property

Set on a hillside above Wells, Stoberry House has breathtaking panoramic views over the city, its Cathedral and the magical and mystical Glastonbury Tor. Originally a coach house, Stoberry is now home to Tim and Frances.

The garden, which has featured in magazines and on television, was designed by Frances to provide colour all year round and is filled with fabulous plants, sculptures, ponds, a box maze, paths and hidden seating areas where guests can revel in the peace and tranquillity which belies the fact that it is only a few minutes walk to the city centre.

Inside, the house is comfortable, stylish and furnished with family antiques and beautiful antique items collected on their travels. The bedrooms and bathrooms are filled with luxurious, handmade bath potions, lotions, robes and slippers and guests can relax in the drawing room, TV room or their own sitting room.

Breakfast is Continental, with fresh fruit and juices, delicious breads and jams, pastries, hams and cheeses, or a delicious cooked breakfast is available on request for a small supplement. There are many restaurants to be enjoyed in Wells or, by prior arrangement, you can have dinner at Stoberry House where there is a very extensive wine list.

The Hosts

Frances has a colonial background and Tim is an international water engineering consultant and they have travelled extensively throughout Africa. Frances has a background in the hotel industry, taught cooking and catered commercially and now combines her love of good food and entertaining to provide guests with a memorable stay.

The Location

So much to see and do! The wonderful city of Wells and its Cathedral, the Bishops Palace and Gardens, Open Market and Vicar's Close are all just a walk away. Wookey Hole Caves and Cheddar Gorge, Glastonbury Abbey and Glastonbury Tor are not to be missed. There are also many excellent walks around Wells and the Quantocks.

Meryl and David Salter
Glen Lodge
Hawkcombe
Porlock
Somerset TA24 8LN
Tel: 01643 863371 or 07786 118933
Fax: 01643 863016
glenlodge@gmail.com
www.glenlodge.net   5950

Finding Us
On entering Porlock, turn left at church onto Parsons Street; approximately ½ mile turn left over bridge. Gate to Glen Lodge is directly ahead.

The Property
Bordering the Exmoor National Park, close to the sea, stands what is quite simply, a special Wolsey Lodge. Nestled amidst the trees, Glen Lodge is a tranquil haven in a picture perfect setting. Built in 1886, the original features have been blended into the warm and welcoming home of Meryl and David Salter.

Set in 21 acres, gardens extend all around tiers with a captivating stream cascading over waterfalls alongside secluded terraces, the croquet lawn and seating areas to while away your time. Exmoor and the coastal paths lead directly from the gardens and the village of Porlock, with its array of shops and tea rooms, is just a short stroll away.

This is a home to relax in and the cosy library, sitting and dining rooms all enjoy the amazing views across the garden to the sea beyond. Tea and cakes are served every afternoon of your stay and are well worth returning home for! Each bedroom has been carefully furnished with all of the finishing touches you would expect of a Wolsey Lodge and your breakfast here will be nothing less than exceptional – the freshly baked muffins are a particular speciality and not to be missed.

The Hosts
David is a master craftsman and spends much of each week working away restoring wooden windows. When at home the garden is his domain and he is a keen sailor and birdwatcher. Meryl is an outstanding cook and keen photographer as well as sharing 'twitching' with David.

The Location
Exmoor is a delight throughout the year – don't miss a walk to Dunkery beacon, charming Porlock Weir, Valley of the Rocks, cliff railway at Lynton, Dunster Castle, Tarr Steps and of course the Exmoor ponies and deer. Take a stroll across the open moors before enjoying a meal and drink at one of the wonderful pubs in the area.

Rooms (per person per night incl. breakfast)

3 Double Rooms (en suite)		**£45**
1 Double Room (private)		**£45**
1 Twin Room (private)		**£45**
Single Supplement		**£15**

Meals

Supper (2 courses)		**£20**
Dinner (3 courses)		**£30**

Opening Times
Closed Christmas & New Year

Payment Options

Facilities & Services

Kerstin & Robert Sharpe
Westleigh Farm
Broomfield, Bridgwater
Somerset TA5 2EH
Tel: 01823 240041 or 01823 452100
Fax: 01823 452101
bookings@westleighfarm.com
www.westleighfarm.com   2953

Finding Us

M5, J25 to Taunton. After Asda on left, turn right at roundabout, over bridge. Left at next roundabout. At 2nd set of lights right lane for Kingston St Mary, continue to KSM, pass Swan Pub, up hill to Pines Cafe. Turn right after Cafe signed Broomfield and Fyne Court. Westleigh is ½ mile on left.

Rooms (per person per night incl. breakfast)

2 Double Rooms (en suite)	**£42.50**
Single Occupancy	**£50**

Meals

Supper	(2 courses)	**£25**
Dinner	(3 courses)	**£30**

Opening Times

Closed mid December to end of February

Payment Options

Facilities & Services

The Property

The warmest of welcomes awaits guests arriving to stay at Westleigh Farm. Set amidst 30 acres and surrounded by Broomfield Common at the foot of the Quantock Hills, this is truly a home from home for guests looking for a peaceful and restful break away from it all.

Spacious and comfortable, the farmhouse has seen much restoration since it became home to Kerstin and Robert in the late 1980s. Downstairs, there is a sitting room complete with deep sofas and a cosy wood burning stove as well as a snooker room with full size table and an atmospheric dining room where guests can enjoy breakfast and dinner. All meals served here are a feast of local and home grown produce and the dinner menu features treats such as home cured gravlax and rack of lamb, rosemary bacon and port sauce – delicious!

The guest bedrooms have views across the fields, en suites and divinely comfortable beds overlaid with fine linen. One bedroom features a balcony and stairs to the pretty garden and orchard where chickens and ducks happily wander. Dining out is another option here and there are several nearby fine restaurants.

The Hosts

Kerstin is Australian and met Robert a consultant psychologist while doing her walkabout around Europe over 30 years ago. Their hobbies over the years have covered all equestrian pursuits, motor racing (following their son from track to track), music, reading, sitcoms, eating and drinking.

The Location

The Quantocks have a wealth of pretty villages to discover as well as Hestercombe House, Fyne Court, Bishops Lydeard steam train, Sheepy's Cider, Dunster Castle, Bishops Lyeard Mill, Kilve Beach (don't forget the lovely cream teas to be enjoyed just above the beach) and of course exploring the Quantocks on foot or bike.

Marie & Victoria Thomas
Binham Grange
Old Cleeve
Minehead
Somerset
TA24 6HX
Tel: 01984 640056 or 07773 328721
mariethomas@btconnect.com
www.binhamgrange.co.uk   **2954**

Finding Us
M5 to Bridgwater, A39 towards Minehead.
Turn right at crossroads after Washford,
signed Blue Anchor & Old Cleeve. Binham
Grange is on left.

Rooms (per person per night incl. breakfast)

1 Super King Double Room (en suite)	£84
1 King Size Double Room (en suite)	£60

Meals

Dinner	£36

Opening Times
Closed Christmas, New Year's Day
& February

Payment Options

Facilities & Services

The Property
Close to the edge of Exmoor, just above Blue Anchor is
Binham Grange, an historic country house offering the most
exceptional accommodation as well as a fine restaurant.
Dating back to 1291 and with connections to nearby
Cleeve Abbey, the house and farm came into your hosts
Marie and Stewart Thomas and their family in 2004 when
they moved lock, stock and cows from Wales and set about
transforming the run-down buildings and gardens.

Guests visiting now delight in discovering this oasis of
calm and tranquillity where little disturbs the complete and
utter peace and quiet. Welcoming, spacious and elegant
rooms offer guests comfortable relaxation and the en suite
bedrooms are furnished with the finest linen and special
finishing touches.

Outside inspired planting of drifts of flowers give way to
a terrace with views across to Exmoor and the coast – the
perfect place to sit awhile and enjoy tea or pre-dinner
drinks. A large vegetable and fruit garden provides much
of the fresh produce for the restaurant and B&B with the
dairy herd on the surrounding 300 acre farm offering their
contribution too. Binham Grange offers one of the best
dining experiences in the area with fine food and wines
from the extensive cellar served in the warm grandeur of the
atmospheric Great Hall – an experience not to be missed.

The Hosts
Whilst Stewart runs the busy farm, Marie and daughter
Victoria look after the house, gardens and guests, together
offering a genuinely warm Welsh welcome to Somerset.
Marie's culinary, decorating and gardening skills ensure
every guests' complete comfort and satisfaction.

The Location
Betwixt the Quantocks and Exmoor Dunster Castle, Cleeve
Abbey, the West Somerset Steam Railway, Hestercombe
Gardens, Tarr Steps and Cothay Manor Gardens are within
reach and Exmoor itself is perfect for walking, cycling and
horse-riding.

The Property

Set against the backdrop of the beautiful Peak District National Park is a gem of a Wolsey Lodge offering the peace and relaxation only found deep in countryside such as that around Martinslow Farm. Throughout the year the welcome is wonderfully warm with blazing fires to cheer your arrival in the winter and stunning views to lift your spirits in the other seasons.

Over 250 years old and Grade II listed, Martinslow Farm was once a donkey station serving the local lead mining industry and today is the comfortable home of Diana and Richard Bloor. It is the perfect location for exploring the Peak District.

In the main house oak beamed rooms with stone floors are comfortably furnished for maximum relaxation whilst across in the stable block, the bedrooms are wonderfully warm with hot water aplenty to rest tired bodies at the end a day's exploring. The two en suite guest rooms, one double and one twin, can be interconnected making them perfect for a family or group of friends. Dinner, if you choose to eat in, and breakfast is delicious and focuses on local produce wherever possible. Being 1000ft above sea level the views from Martinslow Farm are spectacular on a clear day and the garden is surrounded by eight acres of grounds for guests to enjoy.

The Hosts

Diana is a retired physiotherapist and whilst Richard retired from his family's shoe business he is now an accident investigator. They both share a love of the countryside and walking their dogs around the area but above all they truly enjoy entertaining guests in their relaxing and informal home.

The Location

The Peak District is a walkers and cyclists paradise. Close by are Wedgewood Museum, Pottery Museum, Chatsworth House, Haddon Hall, Hardwick Hall, Keddleston Hall and Sudbury Hall.

Richard & Diana Bloor
Martinslow Farm
Winkhill
Leek
Staffordshire
ST13 7PZ
Tel: 01538 304500
richard.bloor@btclick.com
www.martinslowfarm.co.uk   5941

Finding Us

In the centre of Winkhill take sign to Grindon, carry on up steep, narrow lane until you can go no further (ignore crossroads half way up lane). Turn left at triangle junction, the house is 250 yards on right set below the lane.

Rooms (per person per night incl. breakfast)

1 Double Room (en suite)		£47.50
1 Twin Room (en suite)		£47.50
Single Supplement		£20

Meals

Supper	£20
Dinner	£27.50

Opening Times

Closed Christmas

Payment Options

Facilities & Services

Jeffrey & Caroline Bowden
Haughley House
Haughley
Suffolk IP14 3NS
Tel: 01449 673398 or 07860 284722
bowden@keme.co.uk
www.haughleyhouse.co.uk   3982

Finding Us

From the A14, leave at Junction 49. As you proceed up the village street, take the left fork at the village green; Haughley House will be found 100 yards on left hand side.

Rooms (per person per night incl. breakfast)

1 Double Room	(en suite)	**£50-£55**
1 Double Room	(en suite)	**£45-£50**
1 Twin Room	(en suite)	**£50-£55**
Single Occupancy		**£65**

Meals

Supper	**£18**
Dinner	**£28**

Opening Times

Closed occasionally

Payment Options

Facilities & Services

The Property

Set in the historical surroundings of a small village in the heart of Suffolk, the imposing timber framed Haughley House is a late medieval manor.

Inside the manor there is a sumptuous mix of high quality Georgian furniture and exquisite silk lined walls. Antique weapons, fans and plates add to the country house style of a more leisurely age. Guests will be offered tea and home made cakes upon arrival.

All three guest bedrooms are in the oldest part of the house and original oak beams are visible in all three. Both double rooms have period beds (including a majestic mahogany four poster) and en suite shower, whilst the twin room has en suite bath and shower. The comfortable sitting room offers a quiet retreat all year round and a log fire burns in winter.

Outside, the three acre garden has well stocked flower beds and guests can relax in the shade of the ancient Cedar of Lebanon and magnificent beech tree. The orchard and walled kitchen garden provides virtually all the vegetables for the house, whilst the host's own flock of hens provide eggs for the table and their stock provides beef and game for the guests.

The Hosts

Jeffrey is Lord of the Manor and was once a cavalry officer before running a commercial business in London. He and his wife Caroline are keenly interested in hunting, shooting, food and wine. All food is prepared using only the finest ingredients and cooked on the Aga.

The Location

The manor is set within a conservation village with a traditional pub. Within 15 minutes of Haughley is the Georgian market town of Bury St Edmunds, 30 minutes to Cambridge and other historical villages and 45 minutes to the heritage coast.

The Property

Take a step back in time into the historic and stunning West Stow Hall. A Grade I listed Tudor house, renovated in the 1840's and now home to Eileen and Andy Gilbert who have made it a perfect B&B retreat. Walk through the ancient Gatehouse and the colonnade linking it to the main house to be greeted by the family dogs and afternoon tea. Spend a while marveling at the magnificent inglenook fireplace – reputedly the largest in Suffolk - and absorbing the history around you.

There are large guest rooms in the main house and in the garden there is a studio which, with its ground floor access, is ideally suited for less mobile guests. Each room is light, spacious and furnished with great care to ensure your stay is simply as comfortable as possible. A good night's sleep is followed by breakfast featuring an array of fine, local fayre.

The gardens feature lavender lined paths, colourful flowers, an orchard and small woods in which to while away your time. As well as being child-friendly, guests can, by arrangement, bring their horses. A wide choice of nearby restaurants and pubs offers a choice of dining.

The Hosts

Andy, a lawyer, commutes into the City every day whilst Eileen was a teacher. Andy's interest in all things steam is evident in the splendid engines parked in the driveway which he enjoys showing to guests. Eileen is a good cook and enjoys welcoming and looking after her guests.

The Location

Historic Bury St Edmunds is a great base for exploring. West Stow Anglo Saxon Village, Ely Cathedral, Fullers Mill Gardens, Newmarket racing and Cambridge are all within easy reach along with the National Trust properties Anglesey Abbey and Ickworth House. Trout fishing, golfing, walking and cycling are great pastimes for holiday makers staying here.

Andrew & Eileen Gilbert
West Stow Hall
Icklingham Road
West Stow
Bury St Edmunds
Suffolk
IP28 6EY
Tel: 01284 728127
eileengilbert54@aol.com
www.weststowhall.com   3961

Finding Us

From M11 take A11 towards Mildenhall. Before Mildenhall, take A1101 to Bury St Edmunds, after 3 miles turn left to West Stow, on entering village West Stow Hall clearly marked on left and on same road as the Anglo Saxon Village, so follow the signs.

Rooms   (per person per night incl. breakfast)

2 Double Rooms (en suite)	**£45-£55**
1 Double/Twin Room (en suite)	**£45-£55**
Single Supplement	**£15**

Meals

Supper (By prior arrangement)	**£15-£20**

Opening Times

Closed Christmas

Payment Options

Facilities & Services

Mrs Sarah Burgoyne
Old Whyly,
East Hoathly,
Sussex BN8 6EL
Tel: 01825 840216
stay@oldwhyly.co.uk
www.oldwhyly.co.uk   1597

The Property

Sweep down the long drive to the mellow, 17th century listed Grade II manor house where a warm welcome awaits you. Here, elegant reception rooms filled with lovely antiques, pictures and flowers, create a relaxing country retreat. Individually decorated bedrooms with fine linen add to the serene atmosphere.

Old Whyly is a place for all seasons. In the spring, the garden comes to life with rhododendrons, azaleas, daffodils and tulips creating a blaze of colour. You can play tennis on the hard court or laze by the secluded swimming pool.

The lily scented terrace, with its rose covered pergola, is well used on sunny days and warm summer evenings, as is the drawing room with the blazing fire in winter. You can also enjoy lovely walks through the adjoining private estate at any time of year.

The Hosts

One of the highlights of staying at Old Whyly is the dining experience. Having studied cooking and flower arranging in Paris and London, Sarah is a passionate cook. She enjoys using home grown produce wherever possible, with eggs laid by her prize winning hens and ducks, and honey from the bees in the orchard.

The Location

Old Whyly is the perfect place to stay for the Glyndebourne opera festival, being less than 10 minutes away. There are many historic houses, castles and villages to visit within easy reach. The medieval county town of Lewes with its art and antique shops is close by, as is Brighton, with its famous Pavilion and seaside atmosphere.

Finding Us

A22 3 miles south of Uckfield continue for further 0.5 mile past Halland then take first left off large Shaw roundabout towards East Hoathly, for 0.5 mile, drive on left with post box. Where drive divides into 3 take the central gravel drive to Old Whyly.

Rooms (per person per night incl. breakfast)

3 Double/Twin Rooms (2 en suite/1 private)	£45-£70
Single Supplement	£30

Meals

Dinner	£32.50

Opening Times

Closed occasionally

Payment Options

Facilities & Services

The Property

Guests staying at Burwash Place will be following in the footsteps of many famous visitors who have enjoyed the tranquil surroundings - Rudyard Kipling, the poet Rev. James Hurdis and Patrick Moore to name just a few. Burwash Place, which dates from 1712, has the air of a traditional English country house and recent renovations have completed its transformation into a comfortable family home for your host Lindsey Green, her daughter and parents.

The dining room overlooks glorious trees in the garden and with its mix of antique and traditional furniture is the perfect place to relax during breakfast. There is a warm, cosy, newly renovated guest lounge. Upstairs the Kipling suite is a large, bright and airy room with a roll top bath, en suite and the most delightful balcony with stunning views. The Eastern Rose room follows its name with a distinctive floral theme and en suite facilities whilst the twin bedded Persian Blue room has a spacious private bathroom close by. Each has a flat-screen television, DVD player and tea making facilities.

A homemade tea marks your arrival and dinner can be enjoyed at the excellent local pubs and restaurants. Guests may use the enclosed, heated swimming pool (May-October) for an early morning or pre-dinner swim.

The Hosts

Lindsey, together with her mother, offers the warmest welcome during your stay here. A French teacher for many years, Lindsey went on to specialise in dyslexia and now offers private tuition. She is widely travelled and a member of a local book club.

The Location

Burwash Place is in an ideal part of East Sussex for guests wishing to visit Kipling's home Batemans and within an hours drive there is Glyndebourne, Bodiam Castle, Scotney Castle, Alfriston Clergy House, Smallhythe Place, Sissinghurst Castle Garden, Pashley Manor Gardens, Sheffield Park Garden, Great Dixter and the Kent & East Sussex Railway, Bluebell Railway and Lavender Line.

Lindsey Green
Burwash Place
Spring Lane, Burwash
East Sussex TN19 7HX
Tel: 01435 883923
lindsey@burwashplace.co.uk
www.burwashplace.co.uk   **1577**

Finding Us

From North: A21 signed Hastings to Hurst Green. Middle of village, right to Lewes A265 for few miles to Burwash. Pass church, Bear Inn & Oakley Motor Co. on left. After brown sign for Batemans, immediate right into Spring Lane. After $2/3$ mile Burwash Place entrance is on right immediately after long wooden fence & hedge. Down drive, house entrance is door on left of big house.

Rooms (per person per night incl. breakfast)

2 Double Rooms (en suite)		**£50-£60**
1 Twin Room (private)		**£40**
Single Supplement		**£15**

Meals

Breakfast only

Opening Times

Closed occasionally

Payment Options

£ € C TC

Facilities & Services

[5] [icons] WiFi

Rob & Candida Machin
Prawles Court
Shoreham Lane, Ewhurst Green
Robertsbridge, East Sussex TN32 5RG
Tel: 01580 830136 or 07769 708050
    or 07799 576187
info@prawlescourt.com
www.prawlescourt.com   1576

The Property

The promise of 'providing every comfort a guest could expect' is wonderfully fulfilled with a stay at Prawles Court. Your hosts Rob and Candida Machin have created an outstandingly elegant and comfortable home surrounded by 27 acres of gardens and grounds, ideally located on the Kent and Sussex border.

Elizabethan in origin, Prawles was later extended in the Arts and Crafts style by Nathaniel Lloyd and his admiration for Lutyens' designs is highlighted in the airy rooms and decorative brickwork and windows. Inglenook fireplaces in the beamed drawing room and dining room create an intimate atmosphere to relax in, whilst on warm days the Orangery and gardens are the perfect places to enjoy breakfast or afternoon tea.

The bedrooms are simply sublime! Spaciously laid out, with beautiful furnishings, each is individually designed to offer complete and utter comfort. Homemade biscuits and treats are waiting and fine toiletries ensure you can pamper yourself a little too. Home grown and locally sourced produce characterise breakfast and dinner here, whilst an excellent choice of alternative dining venues are close by.

The Hosts

Building a home at Prawles Court with Candida and their three children, Rob enjoys painting, photography, fine wine, antiques and golf whilst Candida combines her family with her curtain business. Looking after their menagerie of animals, home and garden is enjoyed together.

The Location

Prawles Court is within easy reach of Bodiam Castle, Sissinghurst, Batemans, Scotney Castle, Great Dixter, the towns of Battle and its surrounding 1066 country, Rye, Tenterden and Tunbridge Wells. Coastal walks are 20 minutes drive to the south and walkers can access footpaths from the garden.

Finding Us

From A21 turn left on to A229 to Hawkhurst/Maidstone. After 0.1 mile first right into Merriment Lane. At junction turn right onto B2244. After 1.2 miles turn left for Bodiam & Ewhurst Green. Over steam railway line, 2nd left into Shoreham Lane. Prawles is signed 0.1 mile on right. Follow drive to top.

Rooms (per person per night incl. breakfast)

1 Double Room (en suite)	£70
2 Double/Twin Rooms (en suite)	£65-£80
Single Supplement	£35

Meals

Dinner	from £35

(Occasionally by prior arrangement)

Opening Times

Closed Christmas, New Year and occasionally

Payment Options

Facilities & Services

The Property

Sitting beneath the towering South Downs, Tovey Lodge and its three acres of secluded well tended gardens is the perfect base for exploring all that this area of Sussex has to offer. Renovations to the house by your hosts Roy and Diane Burman and earlier owners have combined to create a comfortable home with a choice of guest rooms all offering modern conveniences and wonderful levels of comfort.

Three spacious bedrooms on the first floor all have their own sitting areas with amazing views over the surrounding countryside, whilst downstairs there are two smaller bedrooms. The rooms all have luxurious en suite facilities and guests have their own sitting room with a comforting wood burning stove where you can relax with the television and an array of books, magazines and DVDs to enjoy.

To complete your stay you may also like to take a dip in the heated indoor swimming pool, sauna and hot tub, especially welcome at the end of a long day's walking. Breakfast is a feast of fruit, cereals and juices followed by traditional full English fare using local sausages and bacon and eggs from the resident hens.

The Hosts

Roy is a retired businessman and Diane a retired fashion designer who, as well as welcoming guests into their home, also own a pub and two lighting shops in nearby Brighton which are run by their sons. Their friendly, quiet manner ensures guests have a peaceful stay with every comfort catered for from the beginning to the end of their stay.

The Location

Despite its size, Ditchling village has a museum, shops and pubs and the Stoneywish Nature Reserve, a vineyard and craft centre. Close by the South Downs offer a walker's paradise whilst several National Trust properties, Lewes, Brighton and Glyndebourne all await exploration.

Diane & Roy Burman
Tovey Lodge
Underhill Lane, Ditchling
Sussex BN6 8XE
Tel: 01273 256156 or 07515 753802
toveylodge@gmail.com
www.toveylodge.co.uk   **1580**

Finding Us

From A23 take A273 towards Hassocks for 1.5miles. Right onto B2112 signed Ditchling for 1.8 miles. Turn right into Beacon Road for 0.8 miles. Turn left into Underhill Lane, then left into Tovey Lodge after 100 yards (first driveway). Please use intercom on third post before the gate so that we can welcome you and open it.

Rooms (per person per night incl. breakfast)

3 Super King Double/	**£40-£85**
Twin Rooms (en suite)	
1 King Size Double Room	**£40-£80**
(en suite)	
1 Twin Room (en suite)	**£40-£80**
Single Supplement	**£15-£70**

Meals

Supper – generous cold platter	**£15**
Dinner – 2 Courses	**£28.50**
– 3 Courses	**£35**

Dinner for groups of 6 or more
(Both by prior arrangement)

Opening Times

Closed 6 January – 7 February

Payment Options

Facilities & Services

Sarah & Geoffrey Blake
Landseer House
Cow Lane, Sidlesham
Chichester, West Sussex PO20 7LN
Tel: 01243 641525
enq@landseerhouse.co.uk
www.landseerhouse.co.uk   1585

Finding Us

From Chichester take A286 West Wittering.
At roundabout take left B2201 (to Selsey).
Turn right B2145 Selsey. Follow sign for
Highleigh and Bird Hospital. Turn right into
Keynor Lane, second turn on left to Cow Lane.
Landseer House is the last house on the right.

The Property

Period materials were brought together to create this fine
Regency Sussex style house, which is recommended by
the Michelin Guide. Within walking distance of Pagham
Nature Reserve/harbour and only 5 miles to Chichester and
West Wittering beach. Situated in a glorious location with
wonderful views towards the Isle of Wight. The peace and
quiet is only punctuated by the sound of birdsong, making
this one of the finest places to completely unwind.

With 21st century comforts all six bedrooms and bathrooms
have their own individual charm. Fine antiques and period
paintings, pretty prints, all combined with modern facilities
such as tea and coffee making, flat screened televisions,
internet access and power showers. One bedroom is
exceptionally spacious, with seating area to enjoy the triple
aspect views over the grounds. The others are smaller but
very comfortable. Twenty yards from the main house, two
suites offer separate sitting rooms and bedrooms/en suite.

Delicious breakfasts are served in the garden room
overlooking the grounds. Magnificent sweeping flower
beds lead to meadowlands with meandering pathways and
seating areas where guests can enjoy the tranquillity.

Rooms (per person per night incl. breakfast)

Additional premium for Goodwood and
local events. Minimum 2 night stay at
weekends between 30 April and 1 October

1 Feature Room	(en suite)	£70-£84
1 Double Room	(en suite)	£53-£65
1 Double/Twin	(private)	£53-£65
1 Double/Twin	(en suite)	£53-£65
2 Suites King/Twin	(en suite)	£78-£90
Single Supplement		£42-£55

Meals

Breakfast only

Opening Times

Open all year

Payment Options

Facilities & Services

The Hosts

Sarah and Geoffrey are charming, relaxed and friendly
hosts with an extensive knowledge of the area and offer
a wealth of local information, as well as recommending
the best places to eat. Geoffrey's background is in fine art
restoration and galleries, composing music and classic cars,
whilst Sarah trained as a ballet dancer and is now a very
keen gardener.

The Location

Perfectly situated for Goodwood, golf, motor and horse
racing. Chichester Festival Theatre and Cathedral.
Fishbourne Roman Palace. Uppark and Arundel Castle.
Sandy beaches, walking, marinas and much more.

The Property

The Thatched House sits amongst other cottages in a picture perfect setting on the slopes of the South Downs and, despite the name, is not thatched. Instead it takes its name from its former life as a beer house and is now home to Guy and Mary Leonard who, having lived in the village for 30 years, moved into and renovated the house in 2006. Dating from the 1800s, the warm interior marries original features and antiques with modern comforts and furnishings.

You will be welcomed by Guy, Mary and their friendly corgi Hollyberry and offered tea in the sitting room where you will probably learn about the latest arrivals at the Wildbrooks wetlands area next door. Bewick and Whooper swans and a myriad of wild fowl arrive throughout the year and the opportunity to take a stroll in the reserve should not be missed.

The cosy guest room can be either a double or a twin and is suitably furnished with a newly refurbished private bathroom just along the landing. A second room is available for friends or a family group. Breakfast here is a joy with local bacon, eggs and sausages as well as fresh fruit and, if requested, smoked salmon or pancakes with pancetta.

The Hosts

Guy and Mary's in-depth knowledge of this area of West Sussex is invaluable to guests that are new to the area. Now retired, Mary worked in the health service and Guy was a businessman and together they share a passion for gardening, regularly hosting Open Garden events and are closely involved with the local community.

The Location

Located in our newest National Park, you are close to Goodwood events and walking on the Downs, exploring the museums and galleries of Chichester, Arundel Cathedral, Castle and Arts Festival, National Trust properties such as Petworth House and enjoying the nearby golf courses.

Guy & Mary Leonard
The Thatched House
Hog Lane
Amberley
Arundel
West Sussex BN18 9NQ
Tel: 01798 831329 or 07949 963939
ma.leonard@tiscali.co.uk   **1579**
www.thatchedhouseamberley.co.uk

Finding Us

Take turning off B2139 into Amberley village, follow road to Black Horse Pub, with pub on right take road on left (Hog Lane - not signed) The Thatched House is 5th house on right, just before chalk path leading to the Wildbrooks. Despite its name the house is not thatched.

Rooms (per person per night incl. breakfast)

1 Double/Twin Room (private)	£45
Additional premium will apply for Goodwood events	
Single Supplement	£20

Meals

Breakfast Only

Opening Times

Closed Christmas

Payment Options

Facilities & Services

Poppy Cooksey and Graham Paul
Uplands House, Upton, Banbury,
Warwickshire OX15 6HJ
Tel: 01295 678663 or 0800 130 3663 or
07836 535538
poppy@cotswolds-uplands.co.uk
www.cotswolds-uplands.co.uk   4996

Finding Us
From M40 south, at J11, follow signs to
Banbury A422, continue on A422 through
Wroxton. After 3.6 miles there is a sign
"Upton House 200 yds", in 10 yds turn right
into drive marked Uplands Farm. Uplands
is first house on right. From M40 north, take
J12. Follow signs to Gaydon, turn left in
village and follow signs to Upton House.
Follow A422, past Upton House and turn
left into drive marked Uplands Farm, 30yds
after junction signposted to Edgehill &
Ratley. Uplands is first house on right.

The Property
Fragrances of lavender, honeysuckle, jasmine and roses
tumbling over golden stone walls and an air of calm greet
guests as they approach Uplands along a drive lined with
ancient lime trees.

Inviting and peaceful, guests can wind down in lovingly
furnished surroundings. Relax in the spacious drawing
room; linger over splendid four course dinners or a lighter
supper accompanied with wonderful wines in the candlelit
dining room, or in summer, dine al fresco on the terrace.

Choose between the fabulous four poster bedroom with its
luxurious en suite bathroom or the Chinese room which
can be a double or twin, both of which enjoy a lovely view
across the parkland, or the smaller but charming double
room overlooking the rose garden and bubbling brook.
Whichever room you choose, be spoilt with fresh flowers,
crisp bed linen, lovely bathroom accessories and be assured
of a scrumptious breakfast when you wake.

Rooms (per person per night incl. breakfast)

1 Double Room (en suite)	£50
1 Double/Twin Room (en suite)	£55
1 Feature Room (en suite)	£90
Single Supplement	£15

Meals

Supper	£20
Dinner	£30

Opening Times
Closed Christmas and Easter

Payment Options

Facilities & Services

The Hosts
Poppy and Graham love chatting over a glass of wine or
dinner. Poppy is a picture restorer and art historian. Graham
is retired from teaching engineering at Kings College. Both
have been Olympic fencers, are recent world champions
and enthusiastically compete as veterans. Poppy's creative
cooking using fresh local or garden produce, has won
many accolades and she thoroughly enjoys spoiling guests.
Graham's amazing practical skills keep everything
flowing nicely.

The Location
Guests can walk to see the treasures of Upton House. The
National Herb Centre is close by, as is Edgehill, site of the
first battle of the English Civil War. The gardens of Kiftsgate,
Hidcote, Sezincote and Coughton Court are a short drive
away, and Charlecote Park, Compton Verney, Warwick
Castle, Blenheim Palace, Stratford on Avon and Stow on
the Wold and many other Cotswold towns and villages are
easily accessible.

The Property

Set mid way between historic Warwick and Stratford-upon-Avon, in the Vale of Arden, sits a pretty modern Queen Anne style house that offers travellers a tranquil base for exploring this beautiful part of Warwickshire. Austons Down, home to Lucy and John Horner, is surrounded by 100 acres of gardens and grounds where friendly sheep and the family's horses graze together.

A welcoming and delicious afternoon tea is served on your arrival as you start to unwind and relax in the informal and comfortable surroundings of this family home. Many of the rooms have the advantage of overlooking the glorious gardens which extend around the house and the large patio offers some of the best views of the particularly fine roses that bloom here.

Local produce, as well as vegetables and fruit from the garden, feature at both breakfast and dinner, if you chose to eat in. Lucy will provide her guests with a packed lunch if requested.

The Hosts

Lucy and John brought their family up in Austons Down before deciding to open the house to guests. They share a love of horses, classic cars and rare breed sheep.

The Location

Warwickshire and the surrounding counties are rich in visitor attractions to suit everyone. Warwick Castle, Shakepeare's Stratford with its wonderful theatre, Kenilworth Castle, Heritage Motor Museum at Gaydon, Coventry Cathedral plus National Trust properties such as Charlecote House, Upton House, Coughton Court, Baddesley Clinton and Packwood House. Blenheim Palace is within reach as is Bicester Village and golf courses galore.

Lucy & John Horner
Austons Down
Saddlebow Lane
Claverdon
Warwickshire
CV35 8PQ
Tel: 01926 842068
mail@austonsdown.com
www.austonsdown.com   5945

Finding Us

Detailed directions available at time of booking.

Rooms (per person per night incl. breakfast)

1 Feature Room (en suite)	**£55**
1 Double/Twin Room (en suite)	**£50**
1 Double Room (en suite)	**£50**
Single Supplement	**£17.50**

Meals

Supper	from **£20**
Dinner	from **£30**

Opening Times

Closed Christmas, New Year & Easter

Payment Options

Facilities & Services

Carey and Diana Chapman
Priory Steps
Bradford on Avon
Wiltshire
BA15 1NQ
Tel: 01225 862230
priorysteps@clara.co.uk
www.priorysteps.co.uk   5997

Finding Us

Bradford-on-Avon is on the A363,
8 miles south east of Bath, 2 miles north of
Trowbridge. Take the first left, towards Bath,
just north of Bradford town bridge. Turn left,
signed to Turleigh, by thatched cottage.
Priory Steps is 100 yards down on the left.

The Property

Bradford-on-Avon straddles the river on the southern edge
of the Cotswold Hills, and Priory Steps, originally a terrace
of six weavers cottages, enjoys stunning views over the
beautiful historic townscape.

Old leather sofas nestle in the library, perfect for a relaxing
pre-dinner drink. The dining room, with crackling log fire on
chilly evenings, has a door onto the exquisite terraced garden,
filled with fragrant roses, clematis and passion flowers
clambering over wonderful old Cotswold stone walls.

This light, spacious home was purchased from the world
record breaking aviatrix and motor racer, The Hon Mrs
Victor Bruce - the first lady to win the Monte Carlo Rally
Coupe Des Dames in 1928 and the first Englishwoman to
fly solo around the world. Fascinating memorabilia relating
to her exploits are displayed in the house.

Five comfortably furnished bedrooms, including 'Mrs
Bruce's' with its own sitting room, have their own
bathrooms. Priory Steps is perfect for large groups and
house parties.

Rooms   (per person per night incl. breakfast)

2 Double Rooms	(en suite)	**£49-£57**
2 Twin Rooms	(en suite)	**£49-£57**
1 Feature Room	(en suite)	**£49-£57**
Single Supplement		**£28**

Meals

Dinner	**£28**

Opening Times

Open all year

Payment Options

£ C € TC [card] [VISA] [Maestro]

Facilities & Services

[icons]

The Hosts

Carey and Diana have been welcoming Wolsey Lodge
guests to their home since 1987. Diana is an expertly
trained cook and one of her catering jobs included a cricket
season cooking for the committee and VIPs at the Oval!
Carey, a keen local historian and former Chair of the Town
and District tourist associations, will happily advise on the
best places to visit.

The Location

With an ancient Saxon chapel, splendid Norman church,
14th century town bridge with lock-up and Tithe Barn, the
town is a living history of architecture. It is also central for
visiting Bath, Longleat, Lacock Abbey, Castle Combe, the
beautiful gardens at Stourhead, Stonehenge, Avebury, and
the beautiful Cotswolds.

Colin & Liz Legge
Bullocks Horn Cottage
Charlton
Malmesbury
Wiltshire SN16 9DZ
Tel: 01666 577600
bullockshorn@clara.co.uk
www.bullockshorn.co.uk   5964

Finding Us

A429 from Malmesbury take B4040 to
Cricklade through Charlton. Past Horse &
Groom Pub – ½ mile further, turn left signed
Bullocks Horn – No Through Road – on to
end of lane, turn right, first drive on left.

Rooms (per person per night incl. breakfast)

1 Twin Room	(en suite)	**£45**
1 Double/Twin Room (private)		**£45**
Single Supplement		**£10**

Meals

Supper	(2 courses)	**£20**
Dinner	(3 courses)	**£25**

Opening Times

Closed Christmas & New Year

Payment Options

Facilities & Services

The Property

Situated in a tiny hamlet of just four houses and surrounded
by fields, Bullocks Horn Cottage is a delightful 200 year old
house offering a peaceful and tranquil haven on the fringe
of the Cotswolds.

On arrival you are greeted by Liz and Colin with tea and
delicious cakes to help you unwind after your journey. The
cottage is spacious and beautifully decorated and furnished
with fine antique furniture. The bedrooms have en suite or
private bathrooms and simple decor which highlights the
glorious views from the windows of the gardens and fields
beyond.

Both breakfast and dinner are served in the conservatory or
in the cool shade of the garden. Vegetables and herbs are
used from the kitchen garden together with locally sourced
produce. The garden is spectacular - Liz has created a
stunning cottage garden with a collection of special and
unusual plants with paths meandering around the garden
and seating areas that entice you to sit awhile and take
pleasure in your surroundings.

The Hosts

Liz and Colin are a very friendly, interesting couple who
thoroughly enjoy entertaining guests in their home. Liz is a
Cordon Bleu cook and loves gardening and interiors, whilst
Colin is a talented artist with a studio in the garden and
samples of his work can be seen around the house. When
he is not painting he is a keen golfer and fisherman.

The Location

Only a few miles from the historic town of Malmesbury,
Bullocks Horn Cottage is the ideal base for visiting some
of the most beautiful houses and gardens in England.
Malmesbury Abbey, Abbey House Gardens, Westonbirt
Arboretum and Berkeley Castle are all within easy reach.

Christopher & Enid Richmond
Crockerton House
Crockerton Green
Warminster
Wiltshire BA12 8AY
Tel: 01985 216631
stay@crockertonhouse.co.uk
www.crockertonhouse.co.uk   5961

Finding Us

From A36 south of Warminster take A350 (signed Poole, Blandford) past sign for 'Crockerton', Five Ash Lane and Wylye Valley Vineyard. Slow down and take next turning left into slip road and the drive of Crockerton House which is behind the green.

Rooms (per person per night incl. breakfast)

1 Double Room (private)	**£40-£60**
1 Double/Twin Room (en suite)	**£45-£70**
1 Double/Twin Suite (en suite)	**£45-£70**
Single occupancy	**£72-£125**

Meals

Supper (by prior arrangement)	**£20**

Opening Times

Closed Christmas & occasionally

Payment Options

Facilities & Services

The Property

Historic, luxurious, stylish, charming - words that just about sum up Crockerton House, but hardly do it justice. This house needs to be visited and enjoyed to fully appreciate it. It offers everything one could wish for - the warmest of welcomes with delicious afternoon tea, beautiful furnishings and decor, fabulous bedrooms and bathrooms equipped with every modern luxury, and the most attentive hosts.

Originally part of Lord Bath's Longleat Estate, the house dates from 1669 and has been devotedly restored to provide a magnificent retreat for guests. Restful colour schemes enhance the tranquil feel of the house and provide the perfect ambience for a candlelit supper in the beautiful dining room in front of the inglenook fireplace.

Christopher and Enid have many years experience running an hotel in Devon and have used that expertise to great effect to ensure their guests experience the finest hospitality with delicious, mainly organic, locally sourced food supplemented by fresh seasonal fruit and vegetables from their outstanding garden.

The Hosts

Christopher and Enid are a most welcoming couple. Enid was awarded an AA rosette for culinary excellence six years running at their hotel in Devon and Christopher arranged UK tours for 30 years and will be happy to help guests plan their itineraries to make the most of this wonderful area of the country.

The Location

This is the ideal centre for exploring Wiltshire, Somerset and Dorset and is an area brimming with things to do and places to see. Longleat House, Safari Park and Forest, and easy access to Bath, Salisbury, Stonehenge and Stourhead are just a few. There is also the opportunity for bird watching, fishing and horse riding and a choice of three golf courses nearby.

Jennie & Peter Shaw
Hazeland Mill
Bremhill
Calne
Wiltshire SN11 9LJ
Tel: 01249 821998 or 07775 824670
jennie@hazelandmill.co.uk   **5959**

Finding Us

M4 Junction 17, A350 to Chippenham, A4 to Calne. Before reaching Calne take left turn signed Bremhill. Follow lane for 1 mile and take first left turn at Dumb Post Pub. Hazeland Mill is at bottom of hill by river.

Rooms (per person per night incl. breakfast)

3 Double Rooms (en suite)	£55
Single Supplement	£10

Meals

Supper – 2 Courses	£20
Dinner – 4 Courses	£35

Opening Times

Closed Christmas & New Year

Payment Options

Facilities & Services

The Property

The chance to stay in a beautifully restored watermill is rare, so this is a very special opportunity. The restoration, masterminded by Peter, has been sympathetically carried out using old materials and traditional skills. The mill workings are still in place and there is a large glass window looking out onto the mill race complete with a glass panel in the floor to watch the water plummeting below. Hazeland Mill is built on the side of a steep hill in the hamlet of Bremhill, in a beautiful unspoilt valley.

Spacious bedrooms, with en suite bathrooms, are decorated and furnished with luxurious fabrics and fine furniture. There is also a delightful cottage with sitting room and bathroom just opposite the front door of the main house.

The dining room has a lovely wood burning stove and a comfortable sitting room for guests to use. The eight acre gardens include beautifully tended lawns and flower beds with a large vegetable garden. A large terrace offers an alternative dining area or somewhere to just relax and enjoy the views. Jennie is a fine cook who uses home grown fruit and vegetables and locally sourced meat and fish. Breakfast and dinner are not to be missed.

The Hosts

Peter is a commercial property surveyor and enjoys shooting, stalking and fishing whilst Jennie has a background in retail. They are a most welcoming couple who ensure their guests have a wonderful stay and nothing is too much trouble.

The Location

Hazeland Mill is perfectly located for the historic cities of Bath, Devizes and Marlborough. The magnificent Bowood House is within walking distance and there are open air concerts held at Bowood, Lacock and Westonbirt. Longleat House and Wildlife Park, Badminton and the Cotswold Water Park, Westonbirt Arboretum and Avebury are all easily accessible.

Jonathan & Barbara Hall
Hovington House,
Upper Minety, Malmesbury
Wiltshire SN16 9PT
Tel: 01666 860256 or 07860 337969
barbara@babbie.net   **5975**

The Property
Hidden at the end of the village up a long tree lined drive, this beautiful Cotswold house sits in 20 acres of gardens and paddocks, in front of the lovely 15th century church.

A perfect, informal place to unwind, Hovington House boasts a beautiful 30 foot drawing room with blazing fire. Candlelit dinners in the Scottish styled dining hall are another treat. In the summer tea and drinks can be enjoyed in the garden.

The en suite bedrooms are large and comfortable. One has a stunning barrelled ceiling, with views over the churchyard and field, the other is beamed.

Outside, the heated pool is open from May to October and can be used by arrangement.

The Hosts
Jonathan is originally from Kenya and Barbara is Scottish. Both are very well travelled and speak German and French. Jonathan is in property in London but loves shooting and fishing. Barbara has horses and dogs and enjoys tennis, golf and equestrian events. She used to have her own restaurant, and loves cooking with home grown seasonal vegetables, fruit, game and beef from the family farm in Scotland.

The Location
Hovington House is situated between Malmesbury, Tetbury and Cirencester, just 30 minutes from Bath and Cheltenham and 15 minutes from Badminton and Gatcombe. Watersports lakes are 5 minutes away. The source of the Thames and the start of the Thames Walk are nearby, as is Westonbirt Arboretum, with its lovely walks and open air concerts. London is only 1 hour away by train or car.

Finding Us
Leave M4 Motorway J16. Take A3102 towards Wootton Bassett. At 2nd roundabout go straight on and under the M4. Take 1st turning on right (B4696). After 3 miles turn left at Braydon crossroads signed Garsdon (2 miles). At Minety crossroads go straight over and through village for 2 miles to Upper Minety - take 1st turning on right signed Oaksey & Minety Church. Hovington House is 400yds, 4th driveway on the right.

Rooms (per person per night incl. breakfast)

2 Double Rooms (en suite)	**£50**
Single Supplement	**£10**

Meals

Dinner	**£25**

Opening Times
Closed Christmas & New Year

Payment Options

Facilities & Services

Mrs Sheila Virr
Manor Farm House, Ab Lench,
Evesham, Worcestershire WR11 4UP
Tel: 01386 462226
Fax: 01386 462563   **5999**

Finding Us
From Worcester take the A422, turn right to
Flyford Flavel, at Radford turn right again,
follow signs to Lenches. From Stratford
take A422 signed Alcester, then signed
Worcester. After Inkberrow turn left and
follow signs to Lenches. More detailed
directions given by telephone.

Rooms (per person per night incl. breakfast)

1 Double Room	(en suite)	**£45**
1 Twin Room	(private)	**£40**
Single Supplement		**£10**

Meals

Supper (excl. Sunday)	**£21**
Dinner (excl. Sunday)	**£30**
(By prior arrangement)	

Opening Times
Closed Christmas & New Year

Payment Options

Facilities & Services

The Property
Tucked away in the heart of rural England, Manor Farm
House, set in its lovely garden, is a joy to behold. The house
is about 250 years old, built on to a 300 year old cottage.

The much loved house has a comfortable feel in which
guests immediately feel at ease. Two reception rooms and
a study with television are available for guests, who are
impressed by a magnificent Burmese wall hanging in the
drawing room, where tea is served on their arrival. The
main room of the cottage has original beams and a 7 foot
inglenook fireplace, now a 'den' housing a library and
collected treasures including an 8 foot Texan Longhorn,
the longest ever recorded!

There are two lovely guest bedrooms; the double with en
suite bathroom captures the morning sun and has a
wonderful garden view. The twin, with original fireplace, is
a few paces from the private bathroom. Dressing gowns are
provided.

The beautifully laid out garden is at its best in spring when
500 or so daffodils leap into life. Pheasants and badgers
seem to think that Manor Farm House is their home address
and inquisitive cows peer over the garden wall.

The Hosts
Sheila, and her three little dogs, enjoy entertaining. She
spent many happy years working in the City, then in the
U.S.A. and Caribbean in a somewhat different capacity!
An avid theatre-goer, she still retains links with the R.S.C. at
Stratford.

The Location
This is the English countryside at its best, perfect for visiting
the beautiful Cotswolds, Stratford, Worcester, Cheltenham,
and Warwick Castle. There is also easy access to the M5.

The Property

All that is best in English country house hospitality can be found at 18th century Salford Farm House, which sits in the beautiful Vale of Evesham, surrounded by open farmland. Guests are welcomed to this beautifully furnished home with tea in the award winning garden or in winter the sitting room with inglenook fireplace, is the perfect place to unwind.

In this relaxed atmosphere, the bedrooms stand out for their comfort, traditionally elegant style and wonderful views over the garden. Both en suite bedrooms have feature cast iron fireplaces and invigorating power showers. Bedroom one has a bath with shower over and the second bedroom has a bath and a walk-in shower. Each room has sky television for those who may not want to completely switch off from the rest of the world.

The ½ acre garden with unusual herbaceous borders and masses of spring tulips, features a calming fish pool and pergola made from 150 year old deer fencing. There is a two acre demonstration garden of old fashioned roses and unusual herbaceous plants at Richard's farm.

The Hosts

Richard is a fruit farmer and Jane, a retired ballet teacher. Their hospitality is generous, the food delicious (using meat and game from neighbouring Ragley Estate and with fruit featuring highly on the menu!) and they guarantee that their guests take a store of happy memories away with them.

The Location

The beautiful Stratford-upon-Avon Theatre is just 15 minutes; the NEC Birmingham 40 minutes; the Cotswolds and Cheltenham races 40 minutes and Worcester Cathedral is only 30 minutes.

Richard and Jane Beach
Salford Farm House,
Salford Priors, Evesham,
Worcestershire WR11 8XN
Tel: 01386 870000
Fax: 01386 870000
salfordfarmhouse@aol.com
www.salfordfarmhouse.co.uk   5980

Finding Us

From either Stratford-Upon-Avon or Evesham, take A46. Turn off A46 towards Salford Priors. On entering the village turn right opposite the church (signed Dunnington). Salford Farm House is approximately 1 mile on the right. (Look for white stones)

Rooms (per person per night incl. breakfast)

2 Double/Twin Rooms (en suite)	£45
Single Supplement	£10

Meals

Dinner	£28

Opening Times

Open all year

Payment Options

Facilities & Services

The Property

This magnificent listed Georgian Rectory, dating from 1790 and located in the centre of the village of Cradley, is a delight. Retaining many original features and decorated and furnished in period style, Claire and her partner John have overseen the careful renovation of the house to create a beautiful home.

The hall, surmounted by a stunning atrium, has a curving staircase leading to the beautifully decorated bedrooms on the first floor and a guest sitting room with television and open fireplace at the top of the house. The hall leads into the drawing room with its restored fireplace, carved and gilded wooden pelmets and floor to ceiling windows overlooking the garden. Also leading off the hall are the formal dining room with its superbly sophisticated décor adorned with Claire's fabulous paintings, the Library with large sash windows and a scratched inscription on one pane (ask Claire or John about the historical Clerical dispute) and a delightful morning room.

Home grown vegetables and local produce feature in Claire's inspired cooking and she is happy to prepare packed lunches for guests to enjoy whilst they are out and about.

The Hosts

Claire is a renowned artist and accomplished cook with a passion for walking, whilst businessman John, also a talented cook, plays tennis, squash and racket ball. They both love entertaining and looking after their guests and in their spare time enjoy sailing and the theatre.

The Location

At the foot of the Malvern Hills – perfect for keen walkers to explore the Elgar Route and the Worcestershire Way. The Victorian spa town of Great Malvern and horse racing or shopping at Worcester or Cheltenham are within easy reach. The Three Counties Showground is close by as is Eastnor Castle and the Malvern Theatre. Worcester, Hereford and Gloucester each host the annual Three Choirs Festival in turn.

Claire Dawkins & John Miller
The Old Rectory,
Cradley,
Malvern,
Worcestershire, WR13 5LQ
Tel: 01886 880109 or 07920 801701
oldrectorycradley@btinternet.com
www.oldrectorycradley.com　　5958

Finding Us

Junction 7 from M5. Follow signs to Hereford turn off A4103 signed Cradley (opposite Millbank Garage) through village to Old Rectory soon after village shop and Post Office.

Rooms (per person per night incl. breakfast)

3 Double Rooms	(en suite)	**£65-£70**
2 Double Rooms	(private)	**£60**
1 Twin Room	(en suite)	**£65**
1 Family Suite	(private)	**POA**
Single Supplement		**£35**

Meals

Supper	**£25**
Dinner	**£37.50**

Opening Times

Open all year

Payment Options

Facilities & Services

Judith & Graham Bullock
Kateshill House
Redhill, Bewdley
Worcestershire DY12 2DR
Tel: 01299 401563
info@kateshillhouse.co.uk
www.kateshillhouse.co.uk   5940

Finding Us

From Kidderminster, over the bridge, take second turning left and Kateshill House is half way up the hill on right with sign at bottom of drive.

Rooms (per person per night incl. breakfast)

1 Four Poster Double Room (en suite)	£50
3 King Size Double Rooms (en suite)	£50
1 King Size Double /Twin Room (en suite)	£50
2 Double Rooms (en suite)	£47.50
Single Occupancy	£65

Meals

Supper	£25
Dinner	£35

(Both by prior arrangement. Minimum number of guests may apply)

Opening Times

Open all year

Payment Options

Facilities & Services

The Property

Set on the edge of town within easy walking distance of historic Bewdley, Kateshill House is a magnificent Georgian manor house. Thoughtfully refurbished by the current owners and now boasts twenty first century comfort whilst retaining lots of its original grandeur. Graceful and elegant reception rooms with views across the surrounding lawns and countryside offer a haven of tranquillity.

Each of the seven spacious guest rooms have been individually tailored with a blend of antique and contemporary furniture and fine linen all selected to offer the ultimate in comfort, so relaxation here is totally assured.

As stunning as Kateshill House is, it is the magnificent Sweet Chestnut tree in the garden which cannot fail to grab the attention of visitors. One of fifty Great British Trees selected to mark the Queen's Golden Jubilee, it has a girth of some 33 feet, is around 500 years old and occupies a stately ¼ acre of garden. Keen gardeners will appreciate the labour of love that has created the abundant flower beds and borders which reflect the utter splendour of this very special old manor house.

Home baking and a fine breakfast selection will complete a most comfortable stay and, with an array of fine eateries close by, we are confident a stay of any length here will be utterly and delightfully memorable.

Your Hosts

Cooking, entertaining and gardening are host Judith's passions and, when time allows, travel too. Fine attention to detail means that guests' every need is carefully considered and is one of the many reasons why Kateshill House carries accolades for its excellence.

The Location

Within easy reach of Birmingham, Stratford-upon-Avon, Warwick, Ludlow, Cheltenham, and well situated for visiting Stourport Basin, Tenbury Wells, Arley and Bodenham Arboretums, Kinver Edge and the unusual rock houses, Hartlebury Castle, Harvington Hall, Severn Valley Railway, and West Midlands Safari Park.

The Property

Don't be fooled by the name 'The Wold Cottage'. Far from being a humble cottage, this is a magnificent Grade II listed Georgian Manor House, approached along a tree lined drive through mature landscaped gardens and set amidst 300 acres of rolling farmland. Originally a Georgian gentleman's country retreat the house retains many original features and is full of character.

The rooms are spacious, beautifully decorated and furnished with antiques yet exude a wonderful homely ambience. The bedrooms are delightful, with crisp Egyptian linen, comfortable chairs and are equipped with televisions, clock-radios and tea making facilities, one has a large four poster bed, and all have wonderful views of the Yorkshire Wolds. The en suite bathrooms are also beautifully finished with lovely bathrobes and toiletries.

This "deliciouslyorkshire Breakfast Award" winner's meals are sourced using local produce and include vegetables from the garden whenever possible. Complimentary local bottled water, chocolates and biscuits are left in the rooms. A welcome tea with homemade cake is offered between 4pm and 6pm.

The Hosts

Derek and Katrina are friendly and welcoming hosts who enjoy meeting people and providing guests with an unforgettable stay. They have diversified their working stock and arable farm to welcome guests into their beautiful home.

The Location

Superb location for bird watching, walking along the Yorkshire Wolds Way or the Moors, fishing or golf at Ganton. Visit Castle Howard, Sledmere House or York with it's magnificent Minster and the glorious Yorkshire coast is only 7 miles away so perhaps visit Filey or the famous fishing port of Whitby.

Derek & Katrina Gray
The Wold Cottage
Wold Newton
Driffield
East Yorkshire YO25 3HL
Tel: 01262 470696 or 07811 203336
Fax: 01262 470696
katrina@woldcottage.com
www.woldcottage.com   **8960**

Finding Us

From B1249 turn to Wold Newton, in village turn right by pond, round double bend, first on right, down drive past bungalow.

Rooms (per person per night incl. breakfast)

1 Double Room	(en suite)	**£50-£75**
2 Twin Rooms	(en suite)	**£50-£75**

Meals

Dinner	(by prior arrangement)	**£28**

Opening Times

Open all year

Payment Options

£ € C VAT ⬡ VISA ⬡

Facilities & Services

The Property

First-time visitors cannot help but be charmed by this attractive stone house, sitting behind a beautifully manicured topiary hedge with private parking facilities to the side and a beautiful, traditional walled garden and vegetable garden to the rear.

The welcoming reception sets the tone for a totally relaxing and memorable stay. Guest comfort is a priority and a real sense of warmth pervades the comfortable, traditionally furnished book-lined sitting room, even when the large fire is not alight!

A cosy dining room is the perfect place to end the day with a light supper or mouthwatering four course dinner using home grown and fresh local produce. A leisurely breakfast in the sunny breakfast room overlooking the garden is the perfect start to the day, following a blissful night's sleep in luxurious hand made beds.

The Hosts

Colin and Suzy's warm personalities are reflected in their peaceful home, which they enjoy sharing with guests. They both come from farming backgrounds and hospitality is second nature to them as, amongst other things, they have owned and run a renowned hotel rated in the Times 'Top 100'.

The Location

The word idyllic could have been coined for such a location, an area steeped in history and home to James Herriot. There are numerous attractions such as Newburgh Priory, Shandy Hall, the abbeys of Byland, Rievaulx and Fountains, Castle Howard, Nunnington, Benningborough and Newby Halls. There are several racecourses close to hand; antique and art exhibitions and York is just 16 miles.

Colin & Suzy Bell
Newburgh House,
Coxwold, York YO61 4AS
Tel: 01347 868177
Fax: 01347 868177
info@newburghhouse.com
www.newburghhouse.com   8973

Finding Us

A1 North, bypass Boroughbridge on A168 to Thirsk, bypass Thirsk, joining A19 South to York. After 2 miles on the A19 you come to a sign showing Coxwold Byland Abbey & Helmsley turn left to Coxwold. After 4 miles you enter the village at the top end passing the pub on left, head down the hill, over crossroads and 1/4 mile see a lake on your left and we are 1st house on left past the lake.

Rooms (per person per night incl. breakfast)

2 King Double Rooms (en suite)	**£45-£65**
1 Twin Room (private)	**£35-£40**
Single Supplement	**£15**

Meals

Supper - 2 courses	**£24.50**
Dinner - 4 courses	**£37.50**

Opening Times

Closed December 23rd - 28th (Inclusive)

Payment Options

Facilities & Services

Phillip Gill & Anton van der Horst
Shallowdale House
Ampleforth
York YO62 4DY
Tel: 01439 788325
Fax: 01439 788885
stay@shallowdalehouse.co.uk
www.shallowdalehouse.co.uk   8964

Finding Us

Shallowdale House is situated at the western end of Ampleforth, on the turning to Hambleton. Approach on the 'caravan route' from Thirsk via A19, Coxwold and Wass; or A170 Thirsk to Helmsley, turning right 4 miles after Sutton Bank; or B1363 from York, turning left at Brandsby.

The Property

Shallowdale House is the kind of place that, once you have visited, you don't want to share with anyone else because it is so special. This is an outstanding 1960's architect-designed house with huge picture windows to every room, allowing guests to take in spectacular views of the glorious Yorkshire countryside. There is a warm and relaxing atmosphere throughout and a wonderful attention to detail which makes guests return time and time again.

The bedrooms are light, spacious and stylish with all the finishing touches such as television, radio, tea and coffee making equipment, hairdryers and beautiful toiletries, but the best part must surely be waking each morning to the stunning views from the windows.

As if this wasn't enough, Anton and Phillip are the most delightful and attentive hosts one could wish for, with Anton looking after guests and preparing afternoon tea, and Phillip cooking the most exquisite dinners and setting guests up for a days' activities with a hearty breakfast using the finest, and mostly, locally sourced ingredients.

The Hosts

Anton and Phillip have the wonderful ability to make their guests feel they are the most important people in the world. Nothing is too much trouble and they really enjoy providing their guests with an unforgettable experience. They both have a background in art and design which is evident throughout the house and their local knowledge will ensure guests do not miss any of the delights of the area.

The Location

Situated on the southern edge of the North Yorkshire Moors National Park this is a stunning location encompassing moorland, rugged coastline and beautiful countryside with charming villages. Visit Castle Howard, Rievaulx, Byland and Ampleforth Abbeys, Nunnington and Beningbrough Halls, or the historic cities of York and Harrogate which are both close by.

Rooms (per person per night incl. breakfast)

2 Double/Twin Rooms (en suite)	£65
1 Double Room (private)	£52.50
Single Supplement	£35

Meals

Dinner (4 courses)	£39.50

Opening Times

Closed Christmas, New Year & occasionally

Payment Options

Facilities & Services

The Property

Situated in a peaceful area on the edge of the Yorkshire market town of Ripon, visitors to Sharow Cross House enjoy a tree lined vista with views of the cathedral in the distance. Located just opposite Sharow Cross, the National Monument marking the cathedral boundary and the sanctuary it provided to fugitives. This idyllic and relaxing outlook is all part of discovering a beautiful house that was once the country retreat of a 'soap' baron but which is now home to Lyn and Rod Macaulay.

Large and graceful rooms have been carefully renovated to retain original features such as the oak floors, plaster moulding and imposing fireplaces to give a relaxed and homely feel from the moment you arrive. Tea and homemade cakes on arrival can be followed by dinner if you choose – and we think you should. Dining here is a very real treat and Lyn has created a menu that would grace any fine restaurant, featuring traditional and classic choices made from the freshest produce that is deliciously cooked and perfectly served.

Guest bedrooms are spacious with light flooding in through the huge windows. Each room is equipped with White Company toiletries, complimentary water and snacks and the largest guest room makes a perfect family suite with a comfortable sitting area.

The Hosts

Lyn and Rod know just how to make their guests feel welcome, creating a relaxed atmosphere and giving a memorable experience. Lyn is a passionate cook and delights in creating and making delicious meals for her guests and looking after them so they feel truly pampered.

The Location

Ripon is a beautiful city steeped in fascinating history. Visit the local museum, Newby Hall with its stunning gardens, Fountains Abbey, Harrogate, York, the Yorkshire Dales and Moors – all are within easy reach.

Rod & Lyn Macaulay
Sharow Cross House
Dishforth Road
Ripon
North Yorkshire HG4 5BQ
Tel: 01765 609866
sharowcrosshouse@btconnect.com
www.sharowcrosshouse.co.uk   8950

Finding Us

From A1 South take J48, follow Ripon signs past Racecourse on left, at roundabout turn right onto A61, over next roundabout, next roundabout right into Sharow Lane. House is 3rd drive on left, turn into shared drive & immediately right into house. From A1 North take A61 signed Ripon & Thirsk. Turn right off slip road onto A61 Ripon. Follow road for 3 miles at roundabout, turn left into Sharow Lane. Then as above.

Rooms (per person per night incl. breakfast)

3 Double Rooms (en suite)   **£42.50-£47.50**

Single Occupancy   **from £65**

Meals

Dinner   **£22-£26**

Opening Times

Closed Christmas & New Year

Payment Options

Facilities & Services

The Property
Set behind high garden walls in the pretty North Yorkshire market town of Helmsley sits Ryedale House, an elegant Grade II listed Georgian townhouse offering guests a foothold in a bustling town with an escape to the countryside just moments away.

The house is furnished with a mix of antique and contemporary furniture complemented by sculptures, family photographs and paintings as well as many books for guests to while away their time with, perhaps cosy in the sitting room in the winter or relaxing in the garden on a summer's evening.

Affording excellent views across the town to the castle and garden, the guest bedrooms are located on the first and second floor with private bathrooms for each room. Debbie's flair for interior design is evident in the pretty and highly comfortable décor and guests' every comfort has been provided for including Egyptian cotton bed linen, a well-stocked tea tray, hairdryer, bathrobes and toiletries.

Outside the walled garden is a tranquil refuge that belies its town location and meals served alfresco in the summer are sure to be memorable. Breakfast is a typical North Yorkshire feast of local sausage, bacon and black pudding as well as a selection of homemade jams. Choosing to dine here guarantees equally quality fayre although there are numerous local restaurants to visit also.

The Hosts
Mike was brought up in Castle Howard and is a keen sportsman, representing the UK at the 1984 Winter Olympics for luging, and loves golf, tennis and motor biking. Debbie was a dress designer in London before moving to North Yorkshire in 2000 retaining her love of designing and cooking.

The Location
Situated on the southern edge of Yorkshire Moors National Park, Castle Howard, Ampleforth, Rivaulx and Byland Abbeys, Nunnington, Hovingham, Newby and Beningbrough Halls all close by. York, Harrogate, Scarborough, Whitby and Thirsk are not to be missed.

The Honourable Michael & Debbie Howard
Ryedale House
Bridge Street
Helmsley
North Yorkshire
YO62 5DX
Tel: 01439 771981 or 07767 686383
farleyhoward@msn.com   **8947**

Finding Us
On entering Helmsley via the road bridge over the river Rye, Ryedale House stands on the east side of Bridge Street.

Rooms (per person per night incl. breakfast)

1 Super King Double Room (private)	£55
1 King Size Double Room (private)	£55
Single Supplement	£20

Meals

Supper	£25
Dinner	£35

Opening Times
Open all year

Payment Options

Facilities & Services

The Property

A tree lined drive across parkland takes you to Spital Hill where tea and home made shortbread await, setting the scene for your stay - beautiful food and warm hospitality in peaceful rooms with antique furniture.

Comfortable bedrooms and spacious bathrooms that include quality bath essences and towels, are all individually styled and one of them even has a Bechstein piano, which guests are encouraged to play. All enjoy views across the Vale of York, a quilted pattern of fields, copses and farmhouses.

Food is a hobby here where all bread is hand homemade and delights such as roasted figs in pancetta with raspberry vinaigrette dressed salad; noisettes of lamb on a garlicky potato sauce or Ann's own ice cream with Pedro Ximinez dessert sherry are on the menu, followed by leaf teas, infusions and coffee with home made fudge.

The garden ranges from formal with fountain to natural with waterfall. There is also a croquet lawn with mallets and balls available for those determined to fall out with each other!

The Hosts

Ann and Robin, who love boating as well as good food, understand perfectly that guests wish to be insulated from the normal cares of the world and to relax in tranquil informality.

The Location

Spital Hill is only 9 minutes from the A1 and is the perfect stopover for people on north/south journeys. Thirsk is the birthplace of Thomas Lord who gave his name to Lord's Cricket Ground and home to James Herriott, who used to treat our animals. The ruined abbeys of Byland, Fountains and Rievaulx are close by and Harrogate, York, Whitby and Scarborough are pleasant drives.

Robin & Ann Clough
Spital Hill,
Thirsk, North Yorkshire YO7 3AE
Tel: 01845 522273
Fax: 01845 524970
spitalhill@spitalhill.entadsl.com
www.spitalhill.co.uk   8993

Finding Us

Access by a private road marked by two short white posts on the west side of the A19 Thirsk to York road 1 mile south of the A19 (A170)/A168 intersection.

Rooms (per person per night incl. breakfast)

2 Double Rooms (en suite)		£45-£58
1 Twin Room (private)		£42.50-£50
Single Supplement		£15-£20

Meals

Dinner	£36

Opening Times

Closed Christmas & New Year

Payment Options

Facilities & Services

The Property

Situated at the end of a quiet track just a few miles from York is one of the most peaceful locations you could hope to find. Wood House is in a tranquil setting in a glorious part of the world with much to discover and enjoy nearby. This wonderful haven has been totally renovated and now offers all the comforts you could ask for, which combined with its quite exceptional position makes this a Wolsey Lodge to stay at time and again.

The ground floor suite has a king size double or twin beds, shower room and sitting room. Upstairs there is a twin room with en suite bathroom. Both have televisions and DVD players.

The views from the house over the surrounding countryside are a pure joy and make returning here at the end of the day a real pleasure. Relax in the drawing room or roam the garden and paddock where there are areas to sit awhile and just take in the calm of Yorkshire and catch a glimpse of hares, deer and barn owls too. Dinner is sometimes available and there are local and York restaurants aplenty.

The Hosts

As previous Wolsey Lodge hosts in Suffolk and the North York Moors, Tess and Rex understand perfectly how to help you make the most of your stay. Two friendly Labradors are very much part of the family here too.

The Location

Being close to York there is no shortage of things to do; the City and the Minster, museums, river trips and theatres. Outside the city centre are the Racecourse, one of the largest Maize Mazes in the world, Yorkshire Air Museum, Allerthorpe Watersports, Castle Howard, Sledmere House, Burnby Hall, McArthur Glen Designer Outlet, Bramham Horse Trials and much more.

Tess & Rex Chetwynd
Wood House
Dauby Lane, Kexby, York
North Yorkshire YO41 5LJ
Tel: 01904 607534 or 07931 382382
stay@woodhouseyork.co.uk
www.woodhouseyork.co.uk   8945

Finding Us

From A64 York by-pass, take A1079 eastwards from York. Continue for approx. 3 miles. On reaching the 40 limit and sign saying "Welcome to Kexby" turn immediately right into Dauby Lane. Follow lane for exactly 0.8 miles, turn right onto a small track which is marked only by 2 fence posts with reflective strips set back in the verge. Wood House is then 1/3 mile on this track.

Rooms (per person per night incl. breakfast)

1 King Size Double/	**£47.50-£52.50**
Twin Room (en suite)	
1 Twin Room (en suite)	**£47.50-£52.50**
Single Supplement	**£15-£21**

Meals

Dinner (2 courses)	**£27.50**

Opening Times

Open all year

Payment Options

Facilities & Services

David and Judith Marriott
Thurst House Farm,
Ripponden, Sowerby Bridge,
West Yorkshire HX6 4NN
Tel: 01422 822820
judith@thursthousefarm.co.uk
www.thursthousefarm.co.uk   8983

Finding Us

Ripponden is on the A58, 5 miles east of Junction 22 on M62 and 3 miles west of Sowerby Bridge. At Conservative Club near traffic lights turn up Royd Lane. At top of hill turn right opposite Beehive Inn. Continue straight on for 1 mile. Thurst House Farm is on the right 100 yards past post box. Gateway is beyond blind bend.

The Property

This 17th century listed former farmhouse nestles into the quiet countryside and the surrounding farming community. Warm, welcoming and so hard to leave, it is difficult to believe that an early resident went off to become a general in the American Civil War!

Book-lined walls in the hall, where guests can sit and browse, and an open fire in the sitting room, add to the cosy ambience. Three comfortable bedrooms enjoy lovely views and come with courtesy trays, biscuits, toiletries and fresh flowers for traditional country living. The antique brass double bed is made up with hand-crocheted bed linen and the twin bedroom with its oversize antique white and brass beds has another twin leading off for extra family space. Lie in bed and dream peaceful dreams or wander round the rose-filled garden blooming all summer.

The Hosts

David and Judith's guests experience a real home-from-home. Judith is a trained cook, so you can expect great traditional English cooking. She also makes her own bread, jams and marmalades, so breakfast is a rare treat! Judith also concentrates on the garden, tending the vegetables used in her cooking and making sure she has happy hens!

The Location

The Brontë Museum and the houses used as inspiration in the main novels are just 40 minutes away. Museums abound and The Photographic Museum and Eureka (the children's hands-on activity museum) and Mining Museum are easily accessible.

The Huddersfield Choral Society and Leeds Piano Competition are always worth a visit as are the Calderdale and Pennine Way - a haven for walkers.

Rooms (per person per night incl. breakfast)

1 Double Room	(en suite)	**£35-£40**
1 Twin Room	(en suite)	**£35-£40**
1 Family Room	(en suite)	**£35-£40**
Single Supplement		**£10**

Meals

Dinner	**£25-£27**

Opening Times

Closed Christmas & New Year

Payment Options

Facilities & Services

SCOTLAND AWAITS YOU

Scotland is a truly distinct land. From the snow-capped highlands to the balmy Western shores and to the sophisticated atmosphere of its famous cities and the countryside steeped in history and wildlife, it is a land like no other.

Whatever you have planned - walking, sightseeing, cycling or shopping, you're sure to appreciate returning to your tranquil and welcoming Wolsey Lodge where the promise of good company and dinner, either with your hosts or close-by, will invigorate you for the next day.

From top: Loch Ness; Morar, Scottish Highlands; Glamis Castle, Tayside.

Lynturk Home Farm — Aberdeenshire

John & Veronica Evans-Freke
Lynturk Home Farm,
Alford,
Aberdeenshire AB33 8HU
Tel: 01975 562504
Fax: 01975 563517
lynturk@hotmail.com   **9970**

The Property
Unwind in a haven of tranquillity just a 20 minute drive from Aberdeen airport. This listed farmhouse, built by hostess Veronica's McCombie ancestors in 1762, nestles in its own 300 acres of land where cattle, sheep and horses feed and roe deer wander.

Inside, through the impressive galleried entrance hall, you will find the gracious drawing room, furnished with family antiques and portraits, with a roaring log fire in colder weather. Delicious candlelit dinners and massive breakfasts are served in the tranquil dining room, twinkling with Georgian family silver and glass.

In the morning, you will wake to the sound of the birds and the sight of the deer from your comfortable en suite bedroom with spectacular far reaching hill views in two directions.

The Hosts
Veronica and John are an informal and friendly couple whose outgoing manner immediately helps guests to feel at home. Veronica, a Cordon Bleu cook, is enjoying entertaining extensively again now that her three children are grown up and her horses have become pensioners. John is a Chartered Surveyor who enjoys all sport and country pursuits.

The Location
Lynturk is at the heart of Aberdeenshire with both private and National Trust castles and magnificent gardens close by in every direction. The local village of Alford is home to the Grampian Transport Museum, a heritage centre and a country park with its own miniature railway. Aberdeen is close by, as is the fascinating northern coastline with its pretty fishing villages. Westward, you'll find Speyside and the whisky distilleries and Royal Deeside is 15 minutes away to the south.

Finding Us
From Aberdeen take the A944 towards Alford. Turn left 1 mile before Whitehouse to Tough. Go straight past Tough and after 1 mile Lynturk Home Farm is signed to the left. From Aboyne, take A93 east for 3 miles, left signed Alford, 6 miles over crossroads, 3 miles second Tough sign to right 2 miles, signs on right to Lynturk.

Rooms (per person per night incl. breakfast)
1 Double Room (en suite)		**£45**
2 Twin Rooms (en suite)		**£45**
Single Supplement		**£10**

Meals
Dinner	**£30**

Opening Times
Closed occasionally

Payment Options

Facilities & Services

Jim & Hilary McFadyen
Bealach House
Duror
Argyll PA38 4BW
Tel: 01631 740298
enquiries@bealachhouse.co.uk
www.bealachhouse.co.uk　　　　9934

Finding Us

On the A828 2 miles south of Duror you will see our sign on the main road. turn through the gate (please close the gate after you) and follow the track for one and a half miles.

Rooms (per person per night incl. breakfast)		
2 Double Rooms (en suite)		£50-£60
1 Twin Room (en suite)		£50-£60
Single Supplement		£20

Meals

Dinner (Not on Mondays)	£30

Opening Times

Closed Christmas & New Year

Payment Options

Facilities & Services

The Property

Scottish hospitality is renowned the world over and to visit Bealach House is to understand why. From delicious tea and home made cakes on arrival to a superb dinner in the evening, every comfort has been catered for. Originally a shepherd's croft the house has been added to over the years and is now a substantial home providing luxurious accommodation. You enter through a porch into the large sitting room with wood burning stove and comfortable leather sofas where you can relax with the many books and games available.

The bedrooms are beautifully decorated and furnished and the en suite bathrooms have heated towel rails, fluffy towels and power showers. Bealach is the only surviving house of what was once a small hamlet in a stunning setting surrounded by mountains and forest. Views from the conservatory and bedrooms are glorious and the peace and tranquillity unrivalled. Guests are free to wander and enjoy the views through seven acres of grounds.

The Hosts

Hilary and Jim have spent many years in the hotel business and a yearning to return to Scotland led them to Bealach House where they employ all their expertise to ensure their guests experience the finest care and attention. Hilary is an accomplished cook who ensures her guests enjoy superb food prepared with the freshest ingredients. They are attentive hosts and happily share their knowledge of the area with guests and will help to plan walking and climbing expeditions if required.

The Location

Bealach House is situated midway between Oban and Fort William at Duror in Argyll making it the perfect starting point for visiting the glorious beaches and islands of the West Coast or going inland to the spectacular mountains, glens and lochs of the Highlands.

Robin & Susan Crosthwaite
Cosses Country House,
Ballantrae, Ayrshire KA26 0LR
Tel: 01465 831363
Fax: 01465 831598
staying@cossescountryhouse.com
www.cossescountryhouse.com   9996

Finding Us

From north/south take A77 to Ballantrae. From north go through Ballantrae, over the River Stinchar, then first left (Ballantrae Holiday Park sign). Cosses is 2 miles on the right. From south approach village and turn right before 30mph signs as above.

The Property

Set in twelve acres of woodland and garden, in a hidden valley, this little piece of heaven is the sort of place one loves to discover. Food is always high on the agenda at the beginning and end of your day's exploration of this beautiful area of South West Scotland.

Black labrador, Monty will escort you on a magical walk with views out to sea towards Ireland, Ailsa Craig, the Mull of Kintyre and Arran. Enjoy afternoon tea in a secluded garden, by Chailoch Burn, and drinks in front of a blazing log fire. The two spacious suites across the courtyard and the garden room within the main house are classically decorated and cleverly co-ordinated with every last detail in mind.

The Hosts

Robin and Susan love having people to stay and sharing their passion for superb food and wine. Home grown vegetables, fruit and herbs from the kitchen garden, locally reared meat, game, cheese and freshly caught seafood tempt the taste buds. Susan has written a book about the local food, local history and all that there is to see and do in the South West Scotland. Robin is an accountant with a keen interest in sport, whilst Susan tends the garden and walks the dogs when not looking after guests. Their friends and guests describe them as 'perfect hosts'.

The Location

One hour from Prestwick Airport and low cost airlines, 30 minutes from Irish Ferry Terminals, it is an idyllic country setting, close to the sea, to explore South West Scotland. Whether walking, cycling or motoring through the myriad of quiet roads, visiting the abbeys, castles or standing stones in an area steeped in history, or exploring beautiful gardens, playing golf or fishing, there is something for everyone.

Rooms (per person per night incl. breakfast)

1 Double Room	(en suite)	**£45**
2 Suites	(en suite)	**£55**
Single Occupancy		**£75**

Meals

Dinner	**£35**

Opening Times

Closed Christmas, New Year & occasionally

Payment Options

Facilities & Services

The Property

Chipperkyle is a rather unique gem amongst Scottish country houses. It is a wonderful Georgian Grade B listed Laird's House set in rolling farmland, complete with washhouses and stable courtyard at the back. Your hosts, Willie and Catriona, are justifiably proud of their home and go to great lengths to make their guests feel welcome, serving tea and 'something homemade' on arrival.

Inside, the light and airy rooms are beautifully decorated and furnished, all set against a backdrop of magnificent views in all directions. The double bedroom is comfortable and luxurious and has a large en suite bathroom whilst the twin room has its own private bathroom just one step away. Both bedrooms are furnished with gorgeous white bed linen and the bathrooms with soft, fluffy towels.

Outside there is a large garden with lawns, shrubs and mature trees to walk around, a tennis court in the old kitchen garden and the surrounding fields are home to cattle, sheep, donkeys, pet lambs and the hens that provide the eggs for breakfast. With outdoor sitting areas, guests are invited to enjoy the wonderful, big, often starlit skies, listen to the enchanting bird song and to simply sit back and indulge in total relaxation.

The Hosts

Willie and Catriona are a most hospitable and welcoming couple. Catriona pays special attention to every detail to make your stay enjoyable, and Willie has a wealth of knowledge about Scotland and the local area that makes all the difference to making the most of their wonderful location.

The Location

This is a wonderful area for walking and cycling, top class golf courses, fishing on lochs and rivers, wildlife and bird watching. Nearby, Kirkcudbright is a well known artists' town, whilst Wigtown, like Hay-on-Wye, is a great book centre. Catriona will be able to advise you on the best gardens and museums to visit and there are historic castles and houses to discover and beautiful countryside to explore.

Catriona & Willie Dickson
Chipperkyle
Kirkpatrick-Durham
Castle Douglas
Kirkcudbrightshire DG7 3EY
Tel: 01556 650223
wolseylodge@chipperkyle.co.uk
www.chipperkyle.co.uk   9935

Finding Us

From M6/A74 follow signs to Dumfries/Stranraer. Take ring road round Dumfries taking A75 to Stranraer. After 12 miles at Springholm turn right to Kirkpatrick-Durham 1¼ miles. At KPD crossroads turn left and after 0.8 miles there is a white cottage on right and Chipperkyle is marked on the gate.

Rooms (per person per night incl. breakfast)

1 Double Room	(en suite)	£50
1 Twin Room	(private)	£50
Single occupancy		£75

Meals

Breakfast only

Opening Times

Closed Christmas

Payment Options

Facilities & Services

Frank & Jane Pearson
Applegarth House
Lockerbie
Dumfries & Galloway
DG11 1SX
Tel: 01387 810270 or 07732 127779
janepearson@yahoo.co.uk   **9985**

Finding Us

At J17 of M74 take road to Lockerbie, at roundabout B7076 for Johnstonebridge. 1st right after 1.5 miles to Boreland, after 100 yds turn left back over motorwayway bridge. After 1 mile, right at T-junction, 2nd left to church. House adjacent to church. Do not use satnav.

The Property

Wrapped in history, enchanting Applegarth House, a former Manse, is in a unique and idyllic setting beside the church with views over the River Annan to distant hills.

A warm welcome awaits guests with a fireside tea in winter or in the garden in summer. The drawing room, with magnificent cornicing and antique furniture, and the dining room facing west for amazing sunsets, are off the hall with its grand piano. The sweeping staircase leads up to perfect, country style B&B guest accommodation, two bedrooms each with en suite, one is a twin and the other can be a twin or double.

The partly walled garden is a delight with old statues and unusual plants. A bluebell wood in May surrounds the Motte and the garden is a haven for many species of birds and red squirrels.

The Hosts

Jane and Frank's guests return time and again to enjoy the peace and serenity. Jane loves her garden and is an excellent cook, so bed and breakfast guests are assured of an inspired supper with fresh fish and local meats. Frank has an in-depth knowledge of farming and the countryside as well as many other interests.

The Location

Applegarth House is close to Lockerbie and scenic Lochmaben, both with excellent golf courses. Fishing and shooting can be arranged locally. Drumlanrig Castle, wonderful statues at Glenkiln, Moffat and the stunning Solway Coast are all close at hand. It is in a perfect position for an overnight stop for those travelling north and south, being only five minutes drive from the motorway.

Rooms (per person per night incl. breakfast)

1 Twin Room (en suite)		**£46**
1 Twin/Double Room (en suite)		**£46**
Single Occupancy		**£56**

Meals

Supper	**£24**

Opening Times

Closed occasionally

Payment Options

Facilities & Services

Michael & Vivien Scott
Windmill House
Coltbridge Gardens
Edinburgh EH12 6AQ
Tel: 0131 3460024
windmillhouse@talktalk.net   **9957**

The Property

With Windmill House sitting quietly on a hill surrounded with wild riverside gardens, sloping gently away to a lush river valley and waterfall, you would be forgiven for thinking that you were in the heart of the countryside, miles from anywhere. But you are actually just a mile, as the crow flies, from the city centre, next door to the National Gallery of Modern Art in Edinburgh.

This surprising, three storey Georgian style house welcomes guests into a pillared entrance hall with a galleried staircase. The elegant yet cosy drawing room and dining room both have open fires and a lovely terrace offers incredible views.

The ultra spacious and inviting guest rooms have deeply comfortable beds promising a blissful night's sleep and easy chairs to relax in. Lovely finishing touches include colour television and video and quality soaps and bath essences together with large fluffy white towels in the luxury en suite with bath and power shower.

The eponymous old stone windmill sits in the two acre garden, which is home to ducks, swans and badgers, who come to be fed every night.

The Hosts

Michael is a builder specialising in Georgian and Victorian restoration as well as new houses and Vivien is an interior designer. They are interesting, charming and gregarious hosts and have created a beautiful home which they enjoy sharing with guests.

The Location

Edinburgh is a cosmopolitan city with a world famous festival, museums, galleries, excellent shopping, many restaurants, bars and cafes literally on the doorstep. Paths lead through the garden to a bridge then onto a riverside walk into the city.

Finding Us

Situated 1 mile west of Princes Street. From Murrayfield Avenue turn into Coltbridge Avenue then into Coltbridge Gardens. At the end of Coltbridge Gardens fork left up hill on private drive then fork left through stone gate pillars signed Windmill House.

Rooms   (per person per night incl. breakfast)

1 Double Room	(en suite)	£55-£75
1 Twin Room	(en suite)	£55-£75
Single Occupancy		£65-£85

(A small supplement may apply during the August festivals)

Meals

Breakfast only

Opening Times

Closed Christmas & New Year

Payment Options

Facilities & Services

The Property

As you arrive in the entrance hall of Greenhead Farm with its welcoming log fire you get the first hint of the pleasures in store for those fortunate enough to stay here. Your journey's end is met with tea and home baked treats served either on a sunny verandah if the weather is fine or in front of the drawing room's warming fire.

The farmhouse dates from c.1840 with loving attention brought to bear on the more recent additions added by your hosts Maggie and Malcolm. Antique furnishings and family portraits adorn the house and plump sofas will draw you to the sitting room to relax and take in the stunning views whilst the abundance of board games and books will inveigle you to linger. The bedrooms are spacious, light and beautifully decorated; each with its own bathroom generously supplied with fluffy towels and bathrobes and scented bath essences.

Outside, there is a lovingly tended garden with croquet lawn, fruit trees and a vegetable garden, which provides food for the table. All this is set in 590 acres of farm and woodland providing enjoyable walks.

The Hosts

Maggie and Malcolm enjoy welcoming their guests as friends. Maggie is an excellent hostess and is a keen gardener and trained cook who loves to use fresh produce from her garden whenever possible. Malcolm is an historian with a wealth of local and Scottish knowledge which he will happily share with guests.

The Location

Greenhead Farm is ideally situated for visiting Edinburgh, Perth and Stirling - cities steeped in history with castles, monuments, museums, galleries and festivals. The world famous golf courses of St Andrews, Gleneagles and Muirfield are within an hours drive and there are excellent walks in the Lomond Hills.

Malcolm & Maggie Strang-Steel
Greenhead Farm
Leslie
Glenrothes
Fife KY6 3JQ
Tel: 01592 840459 or 07814 094818
Fax: 01592 841056
maggie@greenheadfarm.co.uk   **9936**
www.fife-bed-breakfast-glenrothes.co.uk

Finding Us

Leave M90 at exit 5 signed Glenrothes. Follow signs for RSPB Vane Farm on south side of Loch Leven B9097; turn left B920 to Scotlandwell. A911 to Leslie, 1¼ miles farm road on left signed Greenhead of Arnot.

Rooms (per person per night incl. breakfast)

2 Double Rooms (private)		£45-£50
1 Single Room (private)		£50
Single Supplement		£15

Meals

Dinner	£30

Opening Times

Closed Christmas & New Year

Payment Options

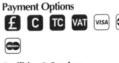

Facilities & Services

Rhoderick & Alison Moncreiff
Tullibole Castle,
By Crook of Devon, Kinross,
Perth & Kinross KY13 0QN
Tel: 01577 840236
holiday@tulbol.demon.co.uk
www.tulbol.demon.co.uk   9960

Finding Us

M90 Junction 6 (Kinross), c5 miles west
along A977, just before Crook of Devon
left along B9097 for one mile, drive on left
through two stone pillars set back from road.
Nearest airport Edinburgh, most convenient
station Inverkeithing.

Rooms (per person per night incl. breakfast)

1 Twin/Double Room (private)	**£50**
Single Supplement	**£10**

Meals

Dinner	**£27**
Supper	**£17**

Opening Times

Closed October - April

Payment Options

Facilities & Services

The Property

The turrets on the entrance tower of this Grade A listed
Scottish castle with peacocks gracing sweeping lawns, are
magically revealed after a winding drive through woodland.

Completed in 1608, the Moncreiff family have lived here
since 1747 and yet their colourful ancestry and the 17th
century architectural features do not overpower this lovely
family home. Guests use the Great Hall with its enormous
log fire and family portraits on the first floor as their own
sitting room, reached by a winding stone spiral staircase.
The generous size comfortable Georgian bedroom is next
door with more stone steps leading down to a newly
refurbished private bathroom.

Outside, two historic ruins - a 9th century Celtic graveyard
and remnants of a ruined medieval church - and a
150 yard 'moat' and doocot sit in parkland. The one acre
kitchen garden is also being restored to provide some
seasonal vegetables.

The Hosts

Rhoderick and Alison are dedicated to the Castle, the
260 acre estate and their many welcome guests. Rhoderick
is Lieutenant to the Chief of the Moncreiff Clan. He and
Alison are collecting family history, re-establishing the Castle
Library and have published a local history book.

The Location

Most of Central Scotland's major attractions are less than
one hour's drive away as are Glasgow, Stirling, Perth,
St. Andrews and Edinburgh with its Festival, Tattoo and
Highland Show. Loch Leven Nature Reserve with bird
watching and trout fishing is on the doorstep as well as lots
of pleasant walks.

The Property

Set in a tranquil Borders village, Skirling House is a truly unique haven of rest and relaxation, where guests are spoilt with award winning gourmet food, fine wines and exceptional hospitality.

Whimsical wrought iron work figures herald the unusual character of the house - its historical artistic connections and Arts & Crafts simplicity brought into sharp relief in the drawing room with a 16th century carved Florentine ceiling, ornate fireplace and decorative door surround. Guests enjoy this lovely room, the cosy book lined study, conservatory and elegant dining room, all of which overlook the garden and woodlands, rolling away to the Borders hills.

Exquisite bedrooms and bathrooms are all highly individual. Warm, welcoming and well furnished with a great sense of style, they possess special individual touches to surprise. Outside, the mature three acre garden includes a tennis court and an idiosyncratic summerhouse, with a floor mosaic set in pebbles and bottle tops!

The Hosts

Bob is a magician in the kitchen and Isobel is the perfect hostess. Their success at Skirling is influenced by their travels and a real understanding of what people need when they are away from home. They are both bright, charming, easy to talk to and have a passion for excellence.

The Location

Nearby attractions include the next village, Biggar, with award winning museums, Victorian Puppet Theatre and amazing Hogmanay bonfire celebration; Dawyck Botanic Gardens, the World Heritage Site of New Lanark and Peebles; the Scottish Borders and Edinburgh and Glasgow with their myriad historic sites and shopping opportunities.

Bob & Isobel Hunter
Skirling House,
Skirling, Biggar,
Lanarkshire ML12 6HD
Tel: 01899 860274
Fax: 01899 860255
enquiry@skirlinghouse.com
www.skirlinghouse.com   9983

Finding Us

Skirling is on the A72, approximately 2 miles north east of Biggar. Skirling House is a dark coloured wood clad house on the west side of the village green.

Rooms (per person per night incl. breakfast)

3 Double Rooms (en suite)		£50-£90
2 Twin Rooms (en suite)		£50-£80

Meals

Dinner	£30-£35

Opening Times

Closed Jan - Feb & 1 week in Nov

Payment Options

Facilities & Services

The Property

Old Kippenross is a magical architectural gem, quite unique in Scotland, tucked away in a sheltered sunny position in a wooded valley beside the River Allan.

The 'ancient tower' was built in 1448 and was confirmed as a Barony in 1507. In 1633 it was extended to a fortified L-shaped tower house. It has been painted pink ever since the battle of Sheriffmuir in 1715, a sign that it was a safe house for Jacobite supporters.

The ground floor is fascinating with a vaulted ceiling, an arched fireplace and a log fire. A spiral stair leads up to the 'Blue Room', a twin bedded room with an en suite bathroom and a small single room for a child or relation. Up again is the 'Tower Bedroom' with a king size double bed and en suite bathroom. The bedrooms are prettily decorated and face south with views to the river where roe deer can often be seen browsing.

Guests can walk beside the river and in the grounds among rare mature trees and abundant wildlife.

The Hosts

Susan and Patrick will give you a warm welcome. They are delighted to share their home with you and they dine with their guests. Susan has a flair for cooking and the delicious dinners, served in the lovely vaulted dining room, often include wild salmon from their own river, local game and organic fruit and vegetables from the garden. Patrick is a keen ornithologist.

The Location

Stirling Castle, the Wallace Monument, Doune Castle and Dunblane Cathedral are very close, and Old Kippenross is ideally placed for visiting the Trossachs National Park, Castle Campbell, Falkland Palace and Gleneagles. Edinburgh and Glasgow can both be reached in under an hour by car, and Old Kippenross is 3 minutes drive from a railway station which has an excellent service to both cities.

Susan & Patrick Stirling-Aird
Old Kippenross,
Dunblane, Perthshire FK15 0LQ
Tel: 01786 824048
Fax: 01786 824482
kippenross@hotmail.com   **9994**
**www.aboutscotland.com/stirling/
kippenross.html**

Finding Us

From north and south go to junction 11 on M9/A9 roundabout. At the roundabout take B8033 and after 500 yards turn right over dual carriageway and into entrance by stone gatehouse. Go down drive and immediately after bridge take first fork right along gravelled drive.

Rooms (per person per night incl. breakfast)

1 King Size Double Room (en suite)	£50
1 Twin/Super King Double (en suite)	£50
Single Supplement	£15

Meals

Dinner	£30

Opening Times

Open all year

Payment Options

Facilities & Services

The Property

Peace, comfort, tranquillity, delicious organic food and a caring approach to their guests are what Fiona and Colin offer at Mackeanston, their 17th century family home.

Mackeanston faces south to the Gargunnock Hills, with distant views of Stirling Castle and the Wallace Monument, while Ben Ledi rises majestically to the north. The first floor en suite bedrooms are very spacious and furnished with ancient armoires and watercolours painted by the Graham family. The super king master bedroom has a huge bathroom, boasting a double walk-in power shower with seat and grab rail, and bath in the centre of the floor, looking out through the connecting door to the hills beyond!

Breakfast and dinner are usually served in the south facing conservatory overlooking the old walled garden. Guests are welcome to use the all-weather tennis court.

The Hosts

Since 1992 Fiona and Colin have been welcoming guests from all over the world, to their comfortable home. Fiona cooks with flair and enthusiasm using organic home grown fruit, vegetables and herbs, and locally sourced meat, fish and game. Aga baked bread, home made jellies and jams feature at breakfast every day. Colin speaks French, German and Italian and is a qualified Blue Badge Guide. He may also treat you to the skirl of the bagpipes after dinner from time to time!

The Location

Mackeanston House provides an ideal central location from which to tour Scotland. Stirling Castle, Wallace Monument, Falkirk Wheel, Loch Lomond and the Trossachs National Park are within easy reach. As well as enjoying a wonderful rural setting, the cultural delights of Edinburgh and Glasgow are just one hour away by train or car.

Colin and Fiona Graham
Mackeanston House,
Doune, Perthshire FK16 6AX
Tel: 01786 850213
Mobile: 07921 143018
info@mackeanstonhouse.co.uk
www.mackeanstonhouse.co.uk   9980

Finding Us

Exit M9 Stirling-Perth motorway at junction 10; follow A84 to Crianlarich for 5 miles. Before Doune, turn left on to B826 to Thornhill. After 2 miles take farm road on left, then private drive on right, just before farmyard.

Rooms (per person per night incl. breakfast)

1 Super king double (en suite with shower seat)	£50-£52
1 Twin/super king double (en suite)	£50
Single Supplement	£15

Meals

Dinner	(3 courses)	£32
	(4 courses)	£35

Opening Times

Closed Christmas

Payment Options

Facilities & Services

Diah & Douglas McAdam
Cuil-an-Duin,
Ballinluig, Pitlochry,
Perthshire PH9 0NN
Tel: 01796 482287 or 07711 161030
Fax: 01796 482287
diah@cuilanduin.wanadoo.co.uk   9953

Finding Us

From South. Take A9 north from Perth, exit into Ballinluig. Turn left signed Allium Garden Centre, turn left past garden centre entrance into road signed local access only. Drive 1 mile into Cuil-an-Duin through two stone pillars.

From North. Exit into Ballinluig, turn right at sign for Allium Garden Centre. Take left turn after garden centre into road marked local access only. Drive 1 mile into Cuil-an-Duin through two stone pillars.

The Property

An enchanting approach through a majestic cathedral-like avenue of Douglas Firs, opens up to reveal this perfect Arts and Crafts style house, hidden within secret woods.

Classic Scottish hunting lodge ambience is complemented with a rich blend of objets d'art and fine furnishings garnered from Far Eastern travels. A welcoming log fire crackles in the drawing room with the dining room overlooking the ever changing canvas of colour of 24 acres of gardens and wildlife woodlands.

Two bedrooms with imposing antique colonial four posters and the third, a stylish twin, all enjoy en suite or private bathrooms, one also with the luxury of a whirlpool bath. Sink into soft feather pillows and awake with the morning sun to enjoy spectacular views across the Tay Valley to the distant peaks of Schiehallion.

Rooms (per person per night incl. breakfast)

2 Double Rooms (en suite)	£50
1 Twin Room (private)	£45
Single Supplement	£15

Meals

Dinner	£30

Opening Times

Closed Christmas & New Year

Payment Options

The Hosts

Doug and Diah have created a wonderfully relaxed family home. Doug, a keen fisherman and shot, is delighted to advise guests interested in pursuing sport locally. Diah is a charming hostess, making people feel instantly at home. She draws upon her Indonesian background combined with fresh, seasonal, local produce to create exquisite dishes for her guests.

Facilities & Services

The Location

The perfect location for touring or staying close to home. The nearby Pitlochry Festival theatre has a renowned programme; Blair Castle and the Hermitage at Dunkeld, Loch Tummel and Loch Rannoch on the famous "Road to the Isles" are close and the shopping mecca of the Highlands, the House of Bruar are within easy reach. Edinburgh, Stirling, St. Andrews and Loch Ness are also within an hour's drive.

John & Tess Monteith
Essendy House
Blairgowrie
Perthshire PH10 6QY
Tel: 01250 884260 or 07841 121538
johnmonteith@hotmail.com
www.essendy.org   9918

Finding Us

Take A93 out of Perth to Blairgowrie (Glenshee & Braemar). Immediately before 30 mph sign at Blairgowrie, turn left onto B947. Go past Muirton Nursing Home, through standing stones, over bridge with green railings, up hill after bridge and drive is at the top of the hill on the right - look for white metal railings.

The Property

Just beyond Perth, at the southern tip of a string of lochs, sits Essendy House, a B&B bolthole for weary travellers and a haven for wildlife lovers. Home to Tess and John Monteith, Essendy House offers quiet comfort, seclusion and relaxation in abundance and yet close by there is much to see and do. Dating back to 1715 with more modern additions, this white-washed country house is surrounded by rich gardens and farmland beyond.

The guest sitting room offers a relaxing haven at the end of the day whilst the conservatory leading on to the terrace is a welcoming retreat on warm days. The bedrooms and bathrooms are supremely comfortable and attractive with antique furniture, wonderful linen and toiletries. The views from the windows are sure to lure you outside where mature trees, azaleas and rhododendrons are in abundance and all around are dramatic hill views.

Highland hospitality dictates a generous and hearty breakfast served in the elegant dining room or on the terrace to set you up for a day's exploring. Close by there are castles and lochs, including the renowned Loch of the Lowes, famous for its Osprey population

Rooms (per person per night incl. breakfast)

1 Double Room	(en suite)	**£50**
1 Twin Room	(en suite)	**£50**

Meals

Supper	**£25**
(By prior arrangement)	

Opening Times

Closed Christmas & New Year

Payment Options

Facilities & Services

The Hosts

Tess was a Lloyds broker and is now an artist who is pleased to offer guidance to guests if they feel like painting whilst here. John completed a career in the Army and plans to build boats. They enjoy the mountains of Europe and have chalets in the Alps where they spend part of the year.

The Location

Between April and September you have the opportunity to see the Ospreys and on fine days take an energetic hike up Birnam Hill, famed for its link to Macbeth. Fishing, shooting and golf are well catered for and the town of Dunkeld boasts a fine cathedral. Glamis and Blair Atholl Castles are close by and in winter there is skiing at Glenshee (40 minutes away).

Sir Archie & Lady Orr Ewing
Cardross
Port of Menteith
Kippen, By Stirling
Stirlingshire FK8 3JY
Tel: 01877 385223
Fax: 01877 385223
stay@cardrossestate.com
www.cardrossestate.com   9931

The Property

Cardross House is magnificent! For anyone with an interest in historic buildings this is an absolute must. Built in 1598 as a Tower House with later additions, it occupies a commanding position on rising ground above the River Forth with magnificent views in all directions.

On arrival at Cardross House you drive through beautiful parkland to be welcomed first by the family dogs and then by Nicola into what is a wonderful blend of friendly informality and elegant formality - comfy chairs covered with blankets in the outer hall and family portraits covering the walls of the main hall and grand staircase. The house has a particularly fine formal drawing room and dining room both beautifully decorated and furnished with fine antiques; however guests will be served breakfast and dinner in the less formal atmosphere of a delightful small Georgian panelled dining room and be entertained in the evening in the charming library in front of a roaring fire.

The bedrooms are spacious, beautifully decorated and furnished and have wonderful views over the garden. The main bedroom has an en suite bathroom and a small open tower room, with dressing table and stool, leading off it, whilst the second bedroom has a private bathroom.

The Hosts

Archie and Nicola Orr Ewing are a delightful, charming and relaxed couple with a wide range of interests from fishing and shooting to music, art and gardening. They know exactly how to put their guests at ease and ensure their stay is a never to be forgotten experience and are keen to share the glories of this stunning area.

The Location

Easy access from Edinburgh, Glasgow and Perth make this is an ideal location. Both east and west coast attractions are within range as are Loch Lomond and Trossachs National Park. There are wonderful castles at Stirling and Doune, historic Bannockburn and the Wallace Monument to visit, and magnificent mountains to climb.

Finding Us

A811 from Stirling. Take B8034 signposted to Port of Menteith. 2 miles on cross River Forth. Cardross drive 150yds on RIGHT (Yellow Lodge). If coming from Port of Menteith on B8034 go through Dykehead hamlet and Cardross drive is 100yds on LEFT.

Rooms (per person per night incl. breakfast)

1 Twin Room	(en suite)	**£60**
1 Twin Room	(private)	**£55**
Single Supplement		**£15**

10% discount for 2 nights or more
15% discount for 4 nights or more

Meals

Dinner – by prior arrangement   **£30**

Opening Times

Closed Christmas & New Year

Payment Options

Facilities & Services

DISCOVER WALES

Wales is rich in culture and traditions - having its own language and cultural events famous throughout the world.

Wherever you travel in Wales you will find friendly faces, fine food and things to see and do in abundance. And, you will find Wolsey Lodges in some of the most beautiful areas from the spectacular Welsh Marches; to the coastal delights of Pembrokeshire and Cardigan Bay; the majesty of the Snowdonia National Park and the North Wales borderlands.

From top: Whitesands Bay, Pembrokeshire; Dolbadarn Castle, Gwynedd; Cardiff.

Keith & Valerie Harber
Coedllys Uchaf, Llangynin, St Clears,
Carmarthenshire SA33 4JY
Tel: 01994 231455
Fax: 01994 231441
coedllys@btinternet.com
www.coedllyscountryhouse.co.uk 6992

Finding Us

A40 to St. Clears roundabout. Take third exit to traffic lights. Turn left at lights. Approximately 100 yards on, road forks to right (signed Llangynin and Chocolate Farm). Turn right here. Continue for 3 miles to Llangrynin, immediately after 30mph signs, turn left, then turn left after approximately 300 yards for Coedllys Uchaf.

Rooms (per person per night incl. breakfast)

2 Double Rooms (en suite)		**£45-£50**
1 Twin Room (en suite)		**£45-£50**
Single Supplement		**£12.50**

Meals

Light Supper	**£10**
(home made soup & sandwiches)	

Opening Times

Closed Christmas

Payment Options

Facilities & Services

The Property

An idyllic, rural scene greets you at this old farmhouse with duck and peafowl ambling across the courtyard and a riot of colourful annuals and evergreens cascading from tubs and hanging baskets. Nestled in eleven acres of rolling fields and woodlands, Coedllys Uchaf (Upper Woodland Court) offers stunning views of the surrounding countryside.

A sense of sanctuary prevails in every sense at this multi award winning accommodation. Warm and welcoming receptions rooms are beautifully and classically decorated. The sitting room and bedrooms overlook rolling countryside and beautiful woodland, cottage gardens and ponds. Traditional Laura Ashley wallpapers, fabrics and soft furnishings enhance the relaxed, intimate and tranquil atmosphere. All rooms have heavenly, comfortable, welcoming and indulgent antique beds, with Hungarian goose down duvets and pillows and the very best of crisp linens. Wi-Fi, squishy sofas, power showers, slippers, fruit, flowers, Molton Brown products and pamper baskets leave guest in no doubt that they are being completely and utterly spoilt!.

The Hosts

Valerie and Keith offer nothing but the very best; the ultimate in comfort. their guests, return time and again to enjoy their warm hospitality. They both retired from the Police, where they worked for many years in the Royalty Protection Branch. The couple run an animal sanctuary with rescued donkeys, ponies, sheep, miniature Shetland pony, chickens, ducks and pea foul. Guests love the animals and the animals love the guests!

The Location

Carmarthenshire and Pembrokeshire have stunning beaches and breathtaking coastal walks. The National Botanical Gardens of Wales and Aberglasney gardens are close by, as are many National Trust properties and Laugharne, home of Dylan Thomas.

Graham and Johanna Jackson
Maesmor Hall,
Maerdy, Corwen, Conwy LL21 0NS
Tel: 01490 460411
Fax: 01490 460441
maesmorhall@aol.com
www.maesmor.com   **6991**

Finding Us

From LLangollen, travelling west on A5 head for Corwen. After Corwen cross River Dee. Go straight through two sets of traffic lights still on A5. After 2 miles turn left opposite The Goat Pub, over narrow river bridge and gates are in front of you.

The Property

Maesmor Hall is the perfect base from which to explore North Wales, to be as active or as relaxed as you choose, to be a culture vulture or follow a quest into the rich historical past - whilst having superb comfort to come 'home' to.

Documented from the early 1200s, its ancient heritage sits comfortably with all the modern luxuries one could wish for, including an indoor heated swimming pool, with sauna, overlooking the river.

The country house ambience is enhanced with antique and new furniture. Paintings in the drawing room, dining room and oak panelled hall make for a cosy welcome on a winter's day with the fire blazing. Beautiful and spacious en suite bedrooms, brimming with every comfort, have lovely garden views.

Parkland and woodland, carpeted with early snowdrops, border 11 acres of sweeping lawns, croquet lawn, tennis court, summerhouse, a stretch of river and a water garden.

The Hosts

Johanna has a natural flair for welcoming and entertaining guests and for many years ran her own restaurant, so providing delicious food to discerning guests is second nature. Both she and Graham enjoy country life, travel and enjoy the rich cultural diversity of the area.

The Location

Every type of rugged outdoor pursuit (and those of a more gentle nature) is available - from walking to mountaineering; viewing waterfalls to whitewater rafting; golf, lake sailing and windsurfing. The Llangollen Eisteddfod; hot air balloon festivals, open air theatre, concerts; canal or narrow gauge railway journeys; Anglesey, Snowdonia, Chester, Shrewsbury, Caernarfon, Betws-y-Coed and Portmeirion Village are just some of the region's varied attractions.

Rooms (per person per night incl. breakfast)

2 Double Rooms (en suite)	**£45-£50**
Single Supplement	**£15**

Meals

Dinner	**£35**
(By prior arrangement)	

Opening Times

Closed Christmas & New Year

Payment Options

Facilities & Services

The Property

Overlooking the Vale of Clwyd, the gardens surrounding Firgrove are a blend of exotic, colourful and inspired planting that will delight gardening enthusiasts and non-gardeners alike. The house itself is a Grade II listed Georgian gem and home since the mid 1980's to your hosts Philip and Anna Meadway.

The graciousness of a bygone era overlays brightly decorated rooms furnished with antiques, collectibles, art and photographs whilst from every window there are views of the garden and countryside beyond. One guest room is in the main house and the second – the cottage suite – has a separate entrance and a sitting room with a fire. Everything you could wish for has been thought of right down to the home made cake on your arrival.

Dining here is a particular pleasure with a menu offering local, seasonal Welsh produce all cooked to perfection and enjoyed in a relaxed and exceptionally friendly atmosphere. Breakfast features a medley of fresh fruit, cereals, yogurt, ham and cheese as well as a traditional cooked option which, together with Philip and Anna's intimate knowledge of the best places to visit, really will set you up for the day ahead.

The Hosts

Philip, a retired professional runs Firgrove with Anna who had retired several years before from her family's business in Ruthin. Gardening intensively and looking after their many visitors, they enjoy regular forays to France to hunt for new delicacies for their guests.

The Location

Perfectly located in North Wales for walking, exploring, bird watching, cycling and shopping there is the Snowdonia National Park, Ruthin and its Craft Centre, Llangollen with its festivals and the nearby awe-inspiring Pont Cysyllte aquaduct, Roman Chester and its famous 'Rows', Llandudno and Llandegla Forest.

Anna & Philip Meadway
Firgrove
Llanfwrog
Ruthin
Denbighshire LL15 2LL
Tel: 01824 702677 or 07710 251606
Fax: 01824 702677
meadway@firgrovecountryhouse.co.uk
www.firgrovecountryhouse.co.uk 6976

Finding Us

Exit Ruthin on A494 to Bala. At mini roundabout go straight on B5105 signed 'Cerrig y Drudion'. Pass church on right and Ye Olde Cross Keys on left. Remain on road travelling ¼ mile driving uphill. Firgrove is large house set above road on right with large pine trees on roadside.

Rooms (per person per night incl. breakfast)

2 Double Rooms (en suite)	**£45-£55**
Single Supplement	**£20**

Meals

Dinner	**£35**

Opening Times

Usually closed November to February inclusive.

Payment Options

Facilities & Services

The Property

'Absolutely stunning' is the only way to describe the views from this lovely house. Situated on the edge of Lake Bala it is a haven of peace and tranquillity - the perfect place to recharge the batteries and appreciate the glories of this corner of Wales.

The house itself is a spacious Victorian gem which manages to combine many fine original features with the most luxurious modern comforts to provide a memorable experience. There is a sitting room and dining room set aside for guests to relax in, all comfortably furnished and beautifully decorated. The dining room has a Bechstein grand piano which musicians are most welcome to use. A west facing terrace offers breathtaking views across the lake to the Arenig Mountains and dramatic sunsets.

The bedrooms are spacious - two have antique four poster beds - all have fabulous en suite bathrooms with under floor heating. Two have spa baths and walk in power showers, the third has a large bath with shower attachment situated such that it overlooks the lake - excellent for soothing aching limbs after a day's activities. To set you up for the day you will be served a wonderful breakfast using mainly local and organic produce and home baked bread.

The Hosts

Katrina and Peter have great energy and enthusiasm and are dedicated to ensuring their guests have a wonderful stay. Nothing is too much trouble and they are keen to share their love and knowledge of this area. Katrina is from a nursing/midwifery background and Peter has his own business and is based in Stockport.

The Location

Bryniau Golau is on the edge of the Snowdonia National Park, in an area of breathtaking beauty, enhanced by castles and gardens, historic towns and cities. There is easy access to uncrowded shorelines and opportunities for canoeing, sailing, fishing, guided walks and white water rafting for the more adventurous.

Katrina le Saux & Peter Cottee
Bryniau Golau
Llangower
Bala
Gwynedd LL23 7BT
Tel: 01678 521782
katrinalesaux@hotmail.co.uk
www.bryniau-golau.co.uk   6985

Finding Us

From Bala, take B4391 towards LLangynog, follow road around until Bala Lake is visible on right. Turn right on B4403 to Llangower. Pass Bala Lake Hotel on left and after approximately ¼ mile Bryniau Golau is 2nd turning on the left. Go up the tarmac road, over cattle grid and Bryniau Golau is the first house on the right.

Rooms (per person per night incl. breakfast)

1 Double Room, four poster (en suite)	**£50**
1 Double Room (en suite)	**£45**
1 Double/Twin Room (en suite)	**£50**
Single Occupancy	**£55-£65**

Meals

Supper	**£20**
Dinner	**£25**

(Meals available Friday & Sunday nights)

Opening Times

Closed Christmas

Payment Options

Facilities & Services

Lady Hallinan
Cotham Lodge,
West Street, Newport,
Pembrokeshire SA42 0TD
Tel: 01239 820341   **6997**

Finding Us

On the A487 Cardigan to Fishguard road. From Cardigan go through the village, the house is on the right next to the Memorial Hall with entrance gates on the corner. From Fishguard, the house is on the left bend of the hill going down to Newport.

Rooms (per person per night incl. breakfast)

2 Double Rooms	**£45**
(1 en suite/1 private)	
1 Twin Room (private)	**£45**
Single Supplement	**None**

Meals

Dinner	**£25**

Opening Times

Closed Christmas & New Year

Payment Options

Facilities & Services

The Property

This Grade II listed, period dower house built in 1787, is set in delightful grounds overlooking the sea.

Across a small courtyard is a cottage, built at the same time, in the traditional Pembrokeshire manner in stone and flint. It has a 'chimney fawr' (a large fire hearth incorporating a bread oven and water boiler). The cottage has been renovated to a high standard with two bedrooms and bathroom and a downstairs shower room. It has its own sitting room. In the house there is a spacious double room with its own bathroom.

The Host

Lady Hallinan welcomes people to this traditional Welsh family home as if they were house guests. For guests who would wish to eat out on occasion there are good restaurants and public houses in the village, no need to take a car.

The Location

The small ancient borough of Trefdraeth (Newport) with its own Norman Castle is in the Pembrokeshire National Park and easily accessible. It is on the coastal walk, which   stretches both north and south with marvellous seascape walking. Lady Hallinan is happy to advise guests on the many attractions of the area. It is an ideal centre for ornithologists, for exploring the unspoilt countryside, the mountains and seashores of both Cardiganshire and Pembrokeshire. St. David's Cathedral, the National Trust Colby Gardens, ancient castles, monuments and many artists and craft galleries are nearby. It is convenient for the Fishguard/Rosslare ferry and the Paddington/Fishguard train.

Janet Evans
Crug-Glas
Near Abereiddy
Solva, Haverfordwest
Pembrokeshire SA62 6XX
Tel: 01348 831302
janet@crugglas.plus.com
www.crug-glas.co.uk   6983

Finding Us
Situated on the A487 St Davids to Fishguard approx 3½ miles outside of St Davids, pass through village of Carnhedryn, first left half a mile after the village.

Rooms (per person per night incl. breakfast)

3 Double Rooms (en suite)		**£70-£75**
1 Twin Room (en suite)		**£57.50**
3 Suites (en suite)		**£65-£100**

Meals
Dinner (3 courses)   **from £20**

Opening Times
Closed Christmas

Payment Options

Facilities & Services

The Property
If you're looking for a place to stay that has the 'wow' factor then this is it. Beautiful house, stunning location, friendliest hostess and fabulous food combine to ensure you will want to return again and again. Crug-Glas is a tastefully restored Georgian house set in 600 acres of farmland with glorious views in every direction and beautiful gardens to relax in.

There is a wonderful blend of antique and modern furnishings throughout and the bedrooms and bathrooms are sumptuous with huge beds, crisp bed linen and soft bathrobes. There is a recently renovated 'honeymoon suite' on the top floor with beautiful bedroom, sitting room and bathroom with spa bath.

Janet is an amazing cook whose restaurant at Crug-Glas has won significant acclaim. She prepares her menus each day according to what fresh meat, fish or vegetables have been delivered and guests make their choice from a wonderful selection of starters, main courses and puddings and Janet then produces the most wonderful dinners that would tempt the most jaded palate. Crug-Glas is fully licensed and there is an 'honesty bar' in the sitting room so guests can relax over a drink after dinner.

The Hosts
Janet is the most friendly hostess with a ready smile and an instinct for knowing exactly how to spoil her guests. Whilst her husband is busy running the farm Janet is happy to entertain interested guests with the history of the farm which dates back to the 13th century.

The Location
St Davids peninsula is a stunning area with walks along coastal paths and glorious beaches. The tiny St Davids Cathedral is not to be missed and there are Pembroke and Picton Castles to visit along with Skomer and Ramsey Islands for their wildlife and fascinating woollen mills at Tregwynt and Middle Mill.

Paul Gerrard
The Old Vicarage
Norton, Presteigne
Radnorshire, Powys LD8 2EN
Tel: 01544 260038
paul@nortonoldvic.co.uk   **6988**
www.oldvicarage-nortonrads.co.uk

Finding Us

The Old Vicarage is at Norton on the B4355, between Presteigne and Knighton. From Presteigne, the house is the first drive on the right after the church. Full directions on www.oldvicarage-nortonrads.co.uk

Rooms (per person per night incl. breakfast)

2 King Size Double Rooms (en suite)	**£49.50-£56**
1 Super King Size Double/ Twin Room (en suite)	**£49.50-£56**
Single Occupancy	**£78**

Meals

Dinner	**£34.50**

Opening Times

Open all year

Payment Options

Facilities & Services

The Property

The spectacular Welsh Marches countryside is the perfect backdrop for The Old Vicarage, a Gothic style house designed by Sir George Gilbert Scott in the 1860s on the bailey of a Norman castle. Every room inside The Old Vicarage is testament to your host Paul's attention to detail, from the period fixtures such as the restored servants' bells, exquisite gas, oil and electric light fittings, richly coloured wallpaper and fabrics, to the lovingly collected Victorian furniture.

Guests' bedrooms are each uniquely furnished with antiques and offer a complete haven for comfort and relaxation. Both the Green Price room and the Gilbert Scott room have king size double beds, whilst the Burlinson room has a super king size four poster bed. Outside, the landscaped gardens were designed by Chelsea award winner Paul Cooper and guests can enjoy exploring the paths, walkways, follies, pond and waterfall that are to be found in this delightful and tranquil garden.

The Hosts

A relaxed, friendly and welcoming host, Paul is a professional chef who delights in providing food sourced from the local area. A voluntary case worker for the Victorian Society, Paul is always keen to share his love and knowledge of Victorian architecture with his guests.

The Location

Named by Country Life as one of the top ten places to live, Presteigne is a former assize and county town offering an award winning museum and a renowned music festival every August. The house is just a short drive from many attractions offering something for all guests including inspiring walks, National Trust Properties, Michelin starred restaurants and wonderful drives through the Cambrian Mountains to Cardigan Bay.

EXPLORE FRANCE

France is a land of contrasts. Rich culture mingles with heritage and stunning scenery wherever you turn. Snowy alpine peaks, rich and verdant countryside and chic cities offer a wealth of experiences for travellers.

A 'taste of home with a different twist' is how we would describe this handful of exclusive Lodges in that they offer all the welcome and hospitality so synonymous with Wolsey Lodges, combined with the thrill and excitement of uncovering the real charm of their beautiful locations.

Top: Rando Chaine des Pays; below right: Chatanvuax

David and Lesley Craven
Chateau La Cour,
14220 Culey le Patry,
Normandy, France
Tel: 00 33 (0) 2 31 79 19 37
info@chateaulacour.com
www.chateaulacour.com   4394

Finding Us

From Caen or from the south, travel on the D562. At Pont de la Mousse, 5kms south of Thury Harcourt, take D133 for Culey le Patry over the river Orne. Turn left onto D166, then second right onto D211. La Cour is on right, on the approach to village, just after first minor road to the right.

Rooms (per person per night incl. breakfast)

2 King Size Double Rooms (en suite)	€75
1 King Size Double/Twin (en suite)	€75
Single Supplement	€25

Meals

Supper 3 courses (incl. wine)	€36
Dinner 4 courses (incl. wine)	€50

(Both by prior arrangement)

Opening Times

Open all year

Payment Options

Facilities & Services

The Property

South of Caen in the wooded Suisse Normande region, lies the pretty village of Culey le Patry. Chateau La Cour is the largest and oldest property hereabouts, dating back to the 13th century, its façade and interior richly evoking links with Richard the Lionheart.

Beautiful wood panelling, traditional tiled floors and elegant double doors decorated with cast iron work, complement the impressive stone staircase leading to three large bedrooms: 'Papillon' with its sumptuous king size double bed, sofa and private stairs leading to an en suite bathroom; the twin bedded 'Fleur de Lys' with Lloyd Loom chairs, writing desk and stunning en suite with king size bath; and the double 'Rosa' with en suite and window seat from which you can gaze endlessly at the Normandy landscape.

Candlelit four course dinners and informal three course suppers feature locally sourced ingredients with vegetables, herbs and fruits from the lovingly tended potager and wild mushrooms foraged from the forest; and a truly splendid gourmet Continental breakfast prove that the heart of French living is good food and wine. Vegetarians are very welcome!

The Hosts

David and Lesley have created a piece of paradise. They enjoy meeting people and guests relish the real taste of relaxed Normandy life. They also offer a very special 'New Year in Calvados' package which blends the finest French and English traditions – excellent food and wine, log fires and convivial company.

The Location

The area offers a range of outdoor pursuits, including golf and walking and is an excellent base for visiting sophisticated Honfleur, Deauville, Bayeux and the D-Day Landing Beaches. Mont St Michel and Monet's garden are also easily accessible.

Comte and Comtesse de Vanssay
Chateau de la Barre, Conflans sur
Anille, Sarthe F-72120, France
Tel: 00 33 (0) 2 43 35 00 17
info@chateaudelabarre.com
www.chateaudelabarre.com   4393

Finding Us
Take the 'La Ferte Bernard' exit from motorway
A11 (Paris to Le Mans-Nantes). Follow D1 through
Vibraye & Berfay. La Barre is 5.5km after Berfay,
600m on your right, after the turn down towards
Conflans which you do not take. Coming from
Calais via Rouen, take A28 and exit after Le Mans
East, then follow N157 past St. Calais, to the D1 for
about 2km. Turn left into La Barre Drive.

Rooms   (per person per night incl. breakfast)
3 King Size Double Rooms   €160-€208
(en suite)
2 Queen Size Double Rooms €145-€160
(en suite)
1 Twin Room   (en suite)   €125
1 Single Room   (en suite)   €168
Minimum stay 2 nights, special discounts on
3 nights or more

Meals
Supper (excl. Wine)   €65
Dinner (served twice a week)   €120
(Grand Dining Room, champagne, wine,
coffee and brandy included).
(Both upon prior reservation only)

Opening Times
Closed 11 January to 11 March

Payment Options

Facilities & Services

The Property
Experience the gracious hospitality and 'douceur de vivre'
of French aristocracy as guests of Count and Countess de
Vanssay, at Château de La Barre, home to their family
for more than 600 years. Secluded in the midst of a 100
acre private park with fragrant gardens and XVIth century
fortifications, this elegant and authentic Château mixes
rare antiques, fine paintings and vibrant designer fabrics
throughout, creating a chic environment full of warmth and
understated luxury.

Seven magnificent and unashamedly luxurious en suite
rooms and suites are all gilded with sumptuous fabrics,
exquisite linens and precious furniture without compromising
on contemporary comforts!

The Hosts
Twice a week, Guy and Marnie host a 'Grand Siècle'
dinner in their ornate 18th century reception rooms, with
all the family silver and crystal. On other nights, a light
supper can be laid out in the majestic XIVth century 'pièce
à feu', where a game of billiards might be enjoyed under
the watchful eyes of the Fox Terrier, the Weimaraner and
Kakou the macaw parrot.

The Location
Less than 2 hours from Paris and 3 from Caen, this is the
perfect place from which to discover the famous Loire
Valley castles, and also explore the untouched countryside
of the little Loir Valley with its many romantic gardens, XIIth
century Romanesque churches, wineries, colourful farmers
markets and gourmet restaurants.

Sport lovers can enjoy a riding school, tennis court and
3 golf courses nearby and the use of complimentary
bicycles on site. On certain dates, it is even possible to
drive a race car around the Le Mans track!

In the summer, don't miss the classical concerts and
the spectacular Sound & Light show in the medieval
Plantagenet City of Le Mans.

Mr & Mrs Coen Stork
Chateau de Villette
58170 Poil
Burgundy
France
Tel: 00 33 (0)3 86 30 09 13
catherinestork@chateaudevillette.eu
www.chateaudevillette.eu   **4385**

Finding Us

On the N81, between Autun and Luzy.
18km from Autun, turn right onto the D192
for Poil. Drive through the tiny village of Poil
and 2km after leaving the village, turn left for
'Villette'.

Rooms (per person per night incl. breakfast)

5 Rooms	(en suite)	€100-€195
2 Suites	(en suite)	€100-€195

Meals

Evening meals and drinks during the day are
included in the room rate.

Opening Times

Dinner	€55
(Wed & Sat only - by prior arrangement)	
Supper	€19
(e.g Cheese Platter)	

Payment Options

Facilities & Services

The Property

Chateau de Villette offers guests a very special, peaceful
and tranquil haven in a remote country setting amongst the
Morvan Hills. Formerly occupied by French aristocracy
and recently renovated, the chateau has been sumptuously
redecorated with meticulous attention paid to the three
large guest rooms which are furnished with the finest
furniture and linen, have their own private bathrooms and
views across the park.

The 500 acre estate surrounding the chateau has been
carefully cultivated using environmentally friendly farming
and conservation practices to provide stunning scenic
contrasts – centuries old parkland, formal terraces, beautiful
woodland and crystal clear streams merge together to create
an idyllic setting to the perfect relaxing break. Chateau de
Villette organises unique driven game shooting on wild
partridge, pheasant and wild boar.

Food is sourced locally to ensure guests experience the very
best of this region's outstanding culinary delights and fine
wines. A minimum of twenty four hours notice is required
for dinner.

The Hosts

Coen and Catherine Stork share a love of this beautiful
area of Burgundy and they extend a very natural, warm
and enthusiastic welcome to guests that discover the very
special retreat they have created at the Chateau de Villette.
The hosts have an in-depth knowledge of the local area and
delight in sharing this with guests.

The Location

It would be hard to visit this area without visiting the local
vineyards and there is an abundance to choose from.
Alongside this there are local antique markets to explore,
tennis and walking and, by going slightly further afield,
guests can take day trips to Roman churches and private
chateaux not normally open to the public.

The Property

This beautifully restored 16th century Breton manor house is fabulous. Approached along a cool, leafy avenue of trees and surrounded by 7½ acres of peaceful and tranquil gardens it is hard to believe you are only 5 minutes from the town centre with its busy shops and markets. Inside, the use of traditional limewash colours and sumptuous furnishings perfectly enhance the ancient granite building. Both the sitting room and dining room are charming with tall french windows to allow the summer sun to stream in and roaring fires in huge fireplaces keep you warm in winter.

The bedrooms all overlook the baroque courtyard and are individually decorated with beautiful antiques and finds from the local antique/brocante shops, fine linens, and fresh flowers from the garden and each bedroom has its own beautifully decorated en suite bathroom. The gardens, besides being a place of relaxation with quiet spaces and a croquet lawn, provide most of the delicious fruit and vegetables served by Penny. This really is a gem of a house offering the most wonderful hospitality to those fortunate enough to stay here.

The Hosts

Penny and Peter take great pleasure from welcoming guests into their home. Penny is a passionate interior decorator, gardener and cook and a wonderfully warm and generous hostess. Peter, an ex-army officer, thatcher and mountaineer turns his hand to most things in the renovation and development of both the house and garden.

The Location

This area of Brittany is rich in history ranging from megalithic standing stones at Carnac through Roman towns, medieval gardens and chateaux. There are fabulous beaches and coastal scenery around the Crozon peninsular and beautiful Breton villages to visit along with walks, festivals of music, art and theatre.

Peter & Penny Dinwiddie
Manoir de Kerlédan
Route de Kerlédan
29270 Carhaix-Plouguer
Finistère, Brittany, France
Tel: 00 33 (0) 2 98 99 44 63
kerledan@gmail.com
www.kerledan.com   4382

Finding Us

From the east, take first exit for Carhaix off N164. After 200 metres take 3rd exit on roundabout west towards Carhaix. Next roundabout take 3rd exit (southern by-pass). This passes between a Citroen and Peugeot garage. Over next roundabout and down hill. Cinema on left and garden centre on right. Turn left at next roundabout. Manoir de Kerlédan 300 metres on the right.

Rooms (per person per night incl. breakfast)

2 Double Rooms	(en suite)	€45-€52.50
1 Twin Room	(en suite)	€45-€47.50
Single Supplement		€35

Meals

Supper	€25
Dinner	€30

Opening Times

Closed mid November to mid March

Payment Options

Facilities & Services

Australia
Accommodation Guide
The B&B Book – 25th Edition

The B&B Book –The original Guide to wonderful accommodation.

Whatever the style, simple or deluxe, B&B or self contained you are treated as a special guest from the moment you arrive until the time you depart.

"A lifetime of memories."

Available from Book Shops in the UK or Mail Order
Inn Australia PO Box 330 Wahroonga NSW 2076
info@bbbook.com.au

www.BBBook.com.au
ISBN 978-0-9758040-8-7

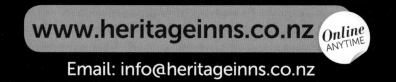

Index

Look up Lodges by Country & County

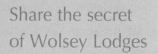

GIFT VOUCHERS
The perfect gift for special people

Share the secret of Wolsey Lodges with friends and family by giving them Wolsey Lodge Gift Vouchers and let them choose a Lodge of their choice from this year's brochure.

Available in denominations of £25 and £50 together with a copy of the current brochure with our compliments.

Ordering is simple - either visit our website www.wolseylodges.com and go to the secure on-line shop, or send a cheque payable to Wolsey Lodges Limited to: Wolsey Lodges Ltd, 9 Market Place, Hadleigh, Ipswich, Suffolk IP7 5DL.

Terms and conditions apply for voucher redemptions. Vouchers can only be redeemed at Wolsey Lodges in the current brochure. To avoid disappointment please check that you hold the most up to date brochure and that you advise the Lodge both at the time of booking and when you arrive that you wish to redeem your vouchers.

From top: West Stow Hall, Suffolk and Kateshill House, Worcestershire - both Wolsey Lodges